The Polecat Survey of Britain 2(

A report on the Polecat's distribution, status and conservation

J.D.S. BIRKS*

The Vincent Wildlife Trust
3 & 4 Bronsil Courtyard, Eastnor, Ledbury, Herefordshire HR8 1EP
www.vwt.org.uk

*Present address: Swift Ecology Ltd., Glen Cottage, Lower Dingle,
West Malvern, Worcs. WR14 4BQ
www.swiftecology.co.uk

This report is published by The Vincent Wildlife Trust and promoted in association with The Mammal Society, which contributed to the survey.

The Vincent Wildlife Trust

 Founded by Vincent Weir in 1975, The Vincent Wildlife Trust is a charity engaged in long-term mammal research and conservation work, primarily in Britain and Ireland. Over the last fifteen years or more, the Trust has invested much of its resources into locating and protecting important summer roosts and hibernation sites for horseshoe bats. Some 50 roosts are being cared for, across South-west England, Wales and Ireland, to ensure long-term protection. Of these nearly half are owned by the Trust.

The VWT also has a strong link with the Mustelids. Originally heavily involved in otter research, today the Trust's current Mustelid studies centre on the polecat and pine marten. The Trust has also played an important role in investigating the status of other mammals, including the water vole and dormouse.

The Vincent Wildlife Trust is a corporate trustee for funds that benefit The Herpetological Conservation Trust, Butterfly Conservation and Plantlife.

For further details: www.vwt.org.uk; Tel. 01531 636441
3 & 4 Bronsil Courtyard, Eastnor, Ledbury, Herefordshire, HR8 1EP.
Email: vwt@vwt.org.uk

Registered charity no. 1112100

The Mammal Society

 The Mammal Society works to protect British mammals, halt the decline of threatened species, and advise on all issues affecting British mammals. The Society studies mammals, identifies the problems they face and promotes conservation and other policies based on sound science. Specifically, The Mammal Society seeks to:

- Raise awareness of mammals, their ecology and their conservation needs
- Survey British mammals and their habitats to identify the threats they face
- Promote mammal studies in the UK and overseas
- Advocate conservation plans based on sound science
- Provide current information on mammals through a range of publications
- Involve people of all ages in the Society's efforts to protect mammals
- Educate people about British mammals
- Monitor mammal population changes

For further details: www.mammal.org.uk; Tel. 0238 0237 874
3 The Carronades, New Road, Southampton, SO14 0AA.
Email: enquiries@mammal.org.uk

Registered charity no. 278918

TABLE OF CONTENTS

1. SUMMARY

This report presents the findings of a three-year survey of the distribution and status of the polecat on mainland Britain. The survey was needed because the polecat's distribution is changing as it recovers from a serious decline caused by heavy culling in the late nineteenth century. Having shrunk to a main stronghold in mid-Wales in the early 1900s, a reduction in trapping pressure since then has allowed the polecat population to expand slowly. This survey is the latest in a series that has tracked this recovery through the twentieth century and into the new millennium.

The survey relied heavily upon help from naturalists and the general public. Many people went to great lengths to supply us with the information that we needed. Because of the occurrence of ferrets and wild-living polecat-ferrets, which are sometimes difficult to distinguish from true polecats, we asked to see visual evidence of specimens so that we could be confident of the identity of each record. This involved people in collecting photographs and carcasses of possible polecats; most of the latter were preserved and donated to the National Museums of Scotland, where a large collection of polecats and ferrets is used for conservation-directed research. Several observations of live polecats were reported; these provided new insights into polecat behaviour in Britain.

The results of this survey confirm that the polecat's encouraging recovery in Britain has continued. The main findings are summarised below:

- 1,273 records of polecats or polecat-ferrets were received from 530 10 x 10km squares during the 2004-2006 survey period; 930 (73.1%) of these records were verified on the basis of visual evidence (typically a dead specimen or a photograph). Road traffic casualties (RTCs) were the most abundant records, comprising 77% of the total.

- Polecats comprised 86.2% of verifiable records from Britain; the remainder were polecat-ferrets. The proportion of true polecats in the recorded population varied significantly between the three countries of Britain, being highest in Wales (95.3%), the polecat's historical stronghold, and lowest in Scotland (40.9%), the only country from which the polecat is believed to have become extinct during the twentieth century.

- Three records of erythristic (a genetically recessive red colour morph) polecats were verified during the survey, from the vice-counties of Chester, Radnor and Brecon.

- The 128 verifiable polecat-ferret records were categorised as either 'dark' or 'pale' on the basis of pelage characters; approximately half (54.7%) were 'dark' specimens very similar in appearance to true polecats.

- Compared with polecat-ferrets, polecats were recorded from more than three times as many 10km squares, and polecat records were twice as abundant as polecat-ferret records in squares occupied by each form.

- Sympatry (co-occurrence) of polecats and polecat-ferrets in Britain was examined at two spatial scales. Both were recorded as present in 30% of 25 x 25km squares occupied by either form. The main areas of sympatry were in North-west England, the North Midlands and central southern England.

- Each vice-county was assigned to one of three 'Polecat Purity Zones' (PPZs) on the basis of the proportion of true polecats among the verifiable records received: PPZ 1 (>95% true polecats) comprised 16 vice-counties in Wales and the English Midlands; PPZ 2 (85-95% true polecats) comprised 11 vice-counties mainly located in central southern England; PPZ 3 (<85% true polecats) comprised 13 vice-counties mainly located around the eastern and southern peripheries of the polecat's British range, with outliers in the North-west of England and Scotland.

- Compared with polecats, polecat-ferrets were significantly under-represented among RTCs during the autumn juvenile dispersal period. Though the underlying mechanism is not known, this observation supports a hypothesis of differences in reproductive fitness and/or survival between the two forms living in the wild in Britain.

- 199 reports of live specimens were received, of which 32% were verifiable. Notably, 68 sightings of possible polecats in gardens provided new information on interactions with people. These included polecats living and breeding in outhouses and under decking, and taking food put out for other wildlife or domestic pets.

- The present survey confirmed a continuation of the twentieth century range expansion by the polecat in Britain. Polecats were verified in 368 10km squares, leading to a cumulative total of 603 10km squares recorded as occupied since 1950. Compared with all previous surveys since 1950, 130 new 10km squares were recorded as occupied, and 85% of these were in England.

- The main areas of recent range expansion were defined by those vice-counties in which >5 new 10km squares were added to the polecat's range since the previous survey: Derby, Bucks, Berks, North Wilts, Dorset, North Hants and South Hants.

- The polecat is now widely re-established in Wales and central England, with outlier populations in northern England and Scotland probably derived from reintroductions.

- A new 2006 population estimate for the polecat in Britain of 46,784 represents an increase of 8,403 (21.9%) at an initial rate of 934 (2.4%) per year since 1997. 92.6% of this population increase has occurred in England.

- The polecat is now a UK BAP priority species. Ten recommendations are made for conservation action.

2. ACKNOWLEDGEMENTS

Any success that this survey might claim is largely thanks to the remarkable commitment of many people willing to contaminate their hands, clothes, vehicles and homes in the interests of natural history. According to the author's contacts in mammalogy across Europe, a survey based on the voluntary collection of polecat road traffic casualties would certainly fail in most countries due to a lack of participants. Thankfully, such an exercise was feasible in Britain due to our special passion for wildlife and our keenness to put time and effort into voluntary wildlife surveys. Even the polecat's famously pungent smell was no deterrent to the brave army of recorders willing to examine, and collect or photograph, carcasses in all states of compaction and decay. So, thanks are due to everyone who rolled up their sleeves and wrinkled their noses in the cause of science; thanks also to those recorders who supplied details to the VWT of their chance encounters with live specimens.

The contributors that made this survey possible are too numerous to thank individually, but some deserve special mention for going that extra mile by producing many records or by co-ordinating survey effort on their patches: Derek Crawley and Nick Mott in Staffordshire; John Dellow in Berkshire; Dan Forman in Glamorgan; Gareth Harris in the Cotswolds; Tim Glover, Phil Court and colleagues over much of the South Midlands; Leonardo Gubert likewise; Jon Hole in Brecknock; Jill Jackson in North Wales; Gareth Jones and Rob Davies in West Wales; Dave Lowe, John Martin and Ruth Dalton in Cumbria; Chris Matcham in Surrey; Mick McCarrick in Bedfordshire; Martin Noble and Tim Sykes in Hampshire; Jane O'Dell and colleagues in Warwickshire; Philip Precey in Derbyshire; John Hodson and Mr. & Mrs. Rea in Worcestershire; Alan Reid and Viv Geen in Shropshire; Phil Richardson in Northants; Sue Tatman and Rob Scrivens in Cheshire; Tammy Stretton in Montgomeryshire; Sophie Tweddle in Dorset; Stephen Westerberg in the North Pennines; Kate Williamson and colleagues in Snowdonia; and Andy Willicome in Wiltshire.

Others who contributed in special ways include Malcolm Lancett, the long-suffering Ledbury-based postman who delivered hundreds of heavy 'polecat boxes' to the VWT's head office; Anna and David Westermann for valuable Health & Safety advice on the involvement of volunteers; staff at English Nature's Bronsil office for receiving and freezing polecat boxes when the VWT office next door was unmanned; The Mammal Society's staff (especially Georgette Shearer and Phoebe Carter) and members who gave much valued help with publicity and the collection of records.

The author is grateful to Vincent Weir and the other trustees for their support and encouragement, and to erstwhile colleagues at the VWT for their good-humoured help during the survey and its write-up: to John Messenger and Dai Jermyn for co-ordinating the collection of polecat carcasses throughout Wales; to Colin Morris for helping similarly in southern England; to Henry Schofield for invaluable support on the IT front; to Kate McAney and Hilary Macmillan (and Lisa Kerslake of Swift Ecology) for proof-reading the turgid prose; and to Hilary Macmillan for also calmly handling the really important stuff so that JDSB could run the survey, and for her tolerance of occasional odd smells at head office.

Finally, special thanks go to Helen and Stacie for huge support at home and for their acceptance of furry surprises in the freezer and a permanently polecat-scented family car; Dogger, Beaver, Tony Laithwaite and Keith Richards provided further support in their own important ways.

3. INTRODUCTION

This report is the latest in a series that describes the changing distribution and status of the European polecat *Mustela putorius* in Britain. Following a steep nineteenth century decline that left the polecat mainly confined to Wales (Langley & Yalden, 1977), distribution-mapping by several authors revealed a slow expansion in range through the twentieth century (Taylor, 1952; Walton, 1964, 1968; Corbet, 1971; Arnold, 1978, 1984, 1993; Teall, 1982; Blandford, 1987; Tapper, 1992; Birks, 1999a). The pattern and causes of this encouraging recovery were reviewed by Birks & Kitchener (1999a) in a wide-ranging report on polecat distribution, ecology, phenotypic variation (including interactions with ferrets *Mustela furo*) and conservation in Britain published by The Vincent Wildlife Trust (copies are still available from the VWT at the time of writing). A more recent, briefer summary of information on polecats and wild-living ferrets in Britain can be found in Birks & Kitchener (2008) and Kitchener & Birks (2008).

This latest report is more modest in scope than its immediate predecessor, and focuses on just two of the recommendations for polecat conservation made by Birks (1999b): distribution-mapping at 10-year intervals was recommended as a means to plot and understand future changes in polecat distribution in Britain; and further assessment of interactions between polecats and wild-living ferrets was recommended in order to monitor patterns of introgression between these two forms within the *Mustela putorius/ furo* group. So, the main aim of this survey was to describe the distributions of polecats and related forms in Britain over the period 2004-2006; further, as part of the survey, we aimed to collect specimens and other evidence to facilitate assessments of introgression through pelage and morphometric examination.

A further aim of this report was prompted by the polecat's new listing in UK conservation: following the UK Biodiversity Action Plan (BAP) Species and Habitat Review, in 2007 the polecat was added to the list of 1149 species and 65 habitats selected as priorities for conservation action under the UK Biodiversity Action Plan (UK BAP, 2007). This should lead to a growth in demand for information and advice on conservation action for polecats from organisations keen to meet their biodiversity responsibilities. Therefore, this report includes a section on suggestions for conservation action, much of which is drawn from the last VWT polecat report by Birks & Kitchener (1999a).

4. SURVEY METHODS

4.1 Survey limits in time and space

This survey covered a recording period from 1st January 2004 to 31st December 2006. During this period, records of polecat-like animals from the *Mustela putorius/furo* group were sought from the mainland of Scotland, Wales and England, and from any islands connected to the mainland that may have been recolonised by polecats, such as Anglesey. Records were not sought from off-shore island groups known to be populated by feral ferrets, such as Shetland and the Hebrides (Kitchener & Birks, 2008). The polecat is not native to Ireland; however, immediately prior to this survey, the presence of a feral ferret population was confirmed in County Monaghan, and further survey work there is now under way (Buckley & Sleeman, 2007).

4.2 Publicity

The importance of gathering records in ways that allowed true polecats to be distinguished from feral ferrets and other polecat-like animals made it essential to base the survey methodology on an appeal for visual evidence of specimens. Starting in late 2003, so as to ensure an effective start in 2004, the survey was publicised in the following ways:

- A double-sided A5 flyer headed 'Pick up a Polecat' (Appendix 1) was distributed widely, to all members of The Mammal Society (TMS), for example; it explained the aims of the survey, invited people to collect specimens or photographs of polecats and stressed Road Safety and Health and Safety considerations when recovering, handling or photographing road traffic casualties (RTCs);
- All the VWT's existing wildlife contacts were contacted by email and invited to participate in the survey;
- Appeals were posted on the websites of both TMS and the VWT, and included in other TMS publications such as *Mammal News* (Anon., 2005);
- Articles were written for national wildlife publications such as *BBC Wildlife* (Birks, 2006) and *Natural World* (Birks, 2004) inviting readers to participate in the survey;
- Illustrated talks advertising the survey were given to a variety of wildlife-related audiences;
- A newsletter providing feedback to all survey contributors was distributed by email every six months, with an invitation to forward it to other interested people and organisations.

Initially the survey requested only records supported by visual evidence. It was soon realised, however, that many interesting and valuable records of possible polecats might be excluded through this strict approach, so the net was widened and other non-verifiable records were accepted.

Contact was established with several local Biological Records Centres (BRCs) in relation to the collection and verification of polecat records. However, because of the emphasis placed on maximising the number of verifiable records, no general trawl of BRCs was undertaken.

4.3 Collection and delivery of carcasses

Publicity material (4.2 above) invited people to contact the VWT after they had recovered the carcass of a polecat-like specimen in order to receive guidance on delivering or sending it to the VWT's head office near Ledbury in Herefordshire, where a large deep freeze was dedicated to the storage of specimens. Subsequently, all specimens in reasonable condition were sent, deep frozen, in batches by courier to the National Museums of Scotland (NMS) to add to the collection of polecat and ferret material established there during the 1990s as a result of the previous VWT polecat survey (Birks & Kitchener, 1999a) and other work by the NMS. This collection of *Mustela putorius/ furo* material is one of the largest in Europe, and is used for a wide range of academic and conservation-directed research. For example, using liver tissue from specimens collected during the 2004-2006 survey, the VWT intends to repeat its collaborative toxicological assessment of the occurrence of rodenticides in British polecats, first undertaken in the 1990s with the NMS and the Centre for Ecology and Hydrology (Shore *et al.*, 2003).

A further advantage of the VWT's head office was its location near the geographical centre of the polecat's British range. This meant that many carcasses could either be delivered to the VWT office by collectors, or collected by arrangement from an informal network of deep freezes (such as those at some County Wildlife Trust offices). Where these low-cost options were not available, arrangements were made for the postage of carcasses to the VWT (see below).

In advance of the survey, the VWT agreed with the Royal Mail acceptable standards for packaging polecat carcasses for postage. These standards were guaranteed by posting the approved packaging material and detailed instructions (see Appendix 2) to those people from whom the VWT had agreed to receive a specimen by post. The main packaging components comprised two sealable (353 x 254mm) plastic bags[1] and a 300 x 240 x 100mm cardboard postal box[2]. The instructions asked contributors to post specimens to the VWT by 'guaranteed next day delivery' early in the week, so as to avoid the risk of carcasses deteriorating in postal sorting offices over the weekend. All postal costs were refunded by the VWT. The total cost per carcass received is shown in Table 4.1.

4.4 Photographic evidence

The widespread use of digital cameras and email meant that visual evidence of possible polecat specimens could be easily emailed to the VWT as jpeg files; in some cases evidence of live specimens was received as digital video footage. Records were also accepted as stills on photographic film. As a clean, efficient, low-cost alternative to the receipt of carcasses, photographic records were especially useful in the case of live specimens or carcasses in a condition unsuitable for preservation (and, therefore, not worth posting). Wherever possible, volunteers intending to photograph carcasses were encouraged to send a series of images illustrating all areas of pelage on the dorsal and ventral surface to enable the VWT to make a judgement about the identity of a specimen (see Kitchener, 2002).

Table 4.1 Typical costs of receiving a polecat carcass via the Royal Mail at the end of 2006

Item	Cost
Materials (cardboard box and two sealable plastic bags)	£1.74
Outward postage (First Class)	£1.70
Return postage (next day delivery <2kg total weight)	£7.40
Total	**£10.84**

[1] Transatlantic Plastics Ltd.: www.transpack.co.uk
[2] Macfarlane Group: www.macfarlanegroup.net

4.5 Verification of records based on visual evidence

A rigorous approach to the verification of records was important in achieving our main survey aims: firstly, the general public's lack of familiarity with polecats (because the species has reappeared only recently in many parts of its range), meant that there was some risk of confusion with similar species such as the feral mink *Mustela vison*; secondly, we needed to separate records of apparently 'true' polecats from those involving feral ferrets or polecat-like specimens displaying some phenotypic evidence of introgression with ferret genes. Whilst these judgements could be made most accurately through an examination of study skins prepared from specimens donated to the NMS, in preparing this report we needed to make a simple categorisation of all verifiable records including those specimens not donated to the NMS because of their poor condition, or those records supported by photographic evidence rather than specimens.

4.5.1 Primary classification of specimens

Drawing upon the experience gained during the previous VWT polecat survey (Kitchener, *et al.*, 1999; Kitchener, 2002), our aim was to assess each specimen on the basis of pelage characteristics in order to place it into either of the following broad phenotype categories:

- True polecat
- Polecat-ferret

Note that in this context we use the term 'polecat-ferret' simply as a label to identify those polecat-like animals that exhibited some 'ferrety' features in their pelage; so the label does not imply any domestic origin; nor does it assume any particular pattern of cross-breeding or genetic introgression between true polecats and ferrets.

The criteria applied when placing records into the two broad pelage categories are shown in Table 4.2. JDSB undertook the majority of verifications by applying these criteria to specimens, photographs or video footage, with some input from A. Kitchener on specimens donated to the NMS; in a few cases, other individuals familiar with the

Table 4.2 Pelage criteria applied when categorising records

Phenotype category	Pelage characteristics
True polecat	Pelage conforms fully to wild polecat type, with none of the polecat-ferret features listed below present; this category included recessive colour morphs such as erythrism
Polecat-ferret	One or more of the following pelage characters* are present: 1. Body fur paler than the wild polecat type (taking account of seasonal pelage variations) 2. Dark fur on face does not reach rhinarium 3. Pale cheek patches and frontal band often very extensive and contrast poorly with darker facial mask, which may be absent (taking account of seasonal pelage variations) 4. Pale throat patch 50mm or more long 5. One or more pale furred paws 6. Scattered white guard hairs over body, especially on hindquarters and tail.

*These characters are taken from Kitchener (2002).

distinctions listed in Table 4.2 made the necessary judgement on a specimen; all other records for which no adequate visible evidence was available were categorised as non-verifiable.

4.5.2 Secondary classification of polecat-ferrets

All specimens classified on visual evidence as polecat-ferrets using the criteria listed in Table 4.2 were given a simple secondary classification based on general body colour: those with a dark body colour approximating to that of a true polecat were labelled 'Dark' polecat ferrets; those with a body colour significantly paler than that of a true polecat were labelled 'Pale' polecat-ferrets. This distinction is somewhat arbitrary because a continuum of pelage variation probably exists between the palest polecat-ferrets and true polecats; nevertheless it is helpful to separate those dark specimens that are difficult for the non-specialist to identify as polecat-ferrets from those that are more obviously not true polecats.

4.5.3 Non-verifiable records

Those records that were not supported by visual evidence were of lesser value because of uncertainty as to their identity as either true polecats or polecat-ferrets. Nevertheless, depending upon the error rate apparent in the sample of verifiable records, any non-verifiable records could be used to indicate the likely presence of the *Mustela putorius/ furo* group in the absence of verifiable records. Therefore, in addition to accepting non-verifiable records during this survey, polecat and ferret records from an annual VWT polecat and mink *Mustela vison* abundance monitoring exercise during 2004-2006 were used as a separate, additional source of distribution data. This monitoring exercise, run by the VWT since 2002, involves hand-picked observers in annual recording of numbers of polecats and mink seen, standardised against miles covered, whilst driving in Britain during September and October. Though verification through visual evidence is not requested as part of this exercise, some recorders did send photographs of specimens and these were included in the sample of verifiable records.

4.6 Storage and curation of specimens

All specimens received by the VWT were stored deep-frozen in plastic bags, each labelled with a unique reference number linking every specimen to a database entry (see 4.7 below).

4.7 Handling and categorisation of records

All records of polecat-like specimens, including ferrets, were entered on an Access database. In addition to entering the basic biological recording elements comprising date, grid reference (usually six figures), location and name of recorder, each record was categorised as follows:

- Verifiability (the nature of visual evidence, if any, used to determine the identity of each specimen)
- Record Type (for example, 'Live Sighting', 'Road Traffic Casualty')
- Whether specimen True Polecat or Polecat-ferret
- Vice-county
- Whether carcass received by the VWT

Distribution maps were produced in DMAP[3]. Note that in this report, when referring to

---

3 DMAP: www.dmap.co.uk

distributional data, the phrase '10km square' is commonly used as shorthand for the more proper term '10 x 10km square'.

4.8 Contribution of records to local and national Records Centres

All verifiable records of polecats or polecat-ferrets from this survey were passed either as Excel files to local Biological Records Centres (BRCs) or entered nationally via the National Biodiversity Network (NBN) Gateway.

5. RESULTS

5.1 The number of records received

The 2004-2006 survey generated 1,273 records of possible polecats and polecat-ferrets from 530 10km squares (see Figure 5.1, which includes additional abundance monitoring data). This compares favourably with the previous VWT survey, in which 1,036 records were gathered from 323 10km squares over an eight-year period (1990-1997). Nearly three quarters of all records received during 2004-2006 were from England (see Table 5.1). 477 records (37.5%) comprised dead specimens received by the VWT at its head office, and 404 of these (31.7% of all records) were donated to the National Museums of Scotland.

5.1.1 Incorporating the VWT's polecat and mink abundance monitoring data

During the 2004-2006 survey window the VWT's polecat and mink abundance monitoring exercise generated an additional 238 records of *putorius/furo* specimens (134 from England, 98 from Wales and 6 from Scotland), only one of which was recorded as a polecat-ferret (from Dorset). These records, which contributed six additional 10km squares, are included in the broad distribution data shown in Figures 5.1 and 5.2. However, because of possible bias inherent in the hand-picked status of recorders, the predominantly unverifiable nature of the records and the narrow seasonal collection period, they are excluded from subsequent analyses in this report.

5.2 Geographical variations in the abundance of records received

Figure 5.2, Appendix 3 and Table 5.1 show, respectively, the extent to which record abundance varied at the 10km square, vice-county and country scale. Notably, Figure 5.2 reveals the likely influence of observer effort on the number of records received as follows: the two 10km squares generating most records (17-25 per square) during 2004-2006 were the adjacent squares SO74 and SO73 on the Herefordshire/Worcestershire border; during the survey the author and survey organiser (JDSB) lived in one and worked in the other, and the relative abundance of records here probably reflects the level of recording activity by him and his local contacts, rather than an unusual abundance of polecats in these 10km squares. In contrast, 82.3% of 10km squares generated four records or fewer over the survey period.

5.2.1 Differences in record abundance between England Wales

During this survey, England generated approximately three times as many records

Table 5.1 The method of verification of possible polecat records received by the VWT from England, Scotland and Wales, 2004-2006

Province	Specimen examined by VWT	Photo examined by VWT	Specimen examined by reliable contact	Film footage examined by VWT	No verification	Total
England	336	321	16	3	250	926
Scotland	7	15			15	37
Wales	134	92	6		78	310
Total	**477**	**428**	**22**	**3**	**343**	**1273**

as Wales (Table 5.1). Notably, many 10km squares in Wales, the polecat's historical stronghold, generated no records at all (Figure 5.2). This might be explained in one of two ways: either polecats have become scarce in Wales and this alone explains the

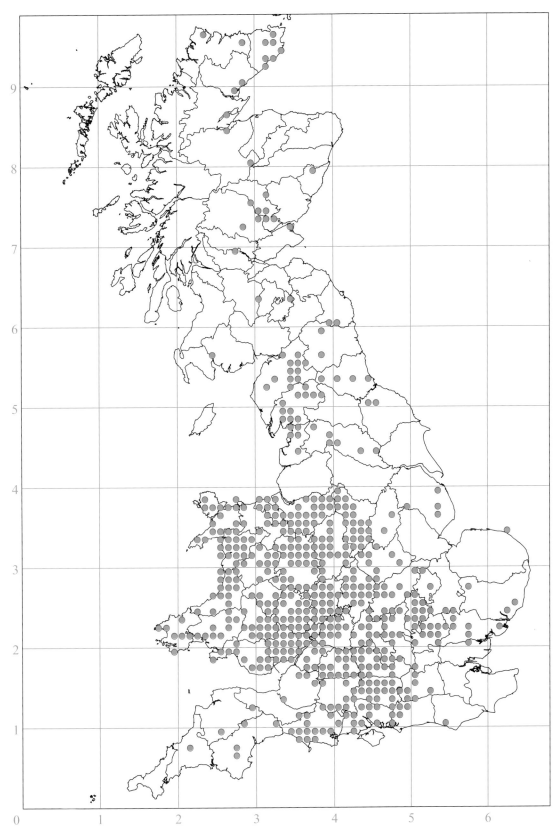

Figure 5.1 The 536 10km squares on mainland Britain from which records (both verifiable and unverifiable) of polecats or polecat-ferrets were received during 2004-2006; these data include an additional six squares from the VWT's separate abundance monitoring exercise; boundaries of Watsonian vice-counties are shown.

paucity of records; or polecats remain common in Wales but records are sparse due to observer effects and other influences. For example, in much of Wales, human population density, road density and traffic densities are low compared with those in the central and southern England, and this is likely to reduce the abundance of polecat records (the VWT's 1990s polecat survey identified a positive association between the density of

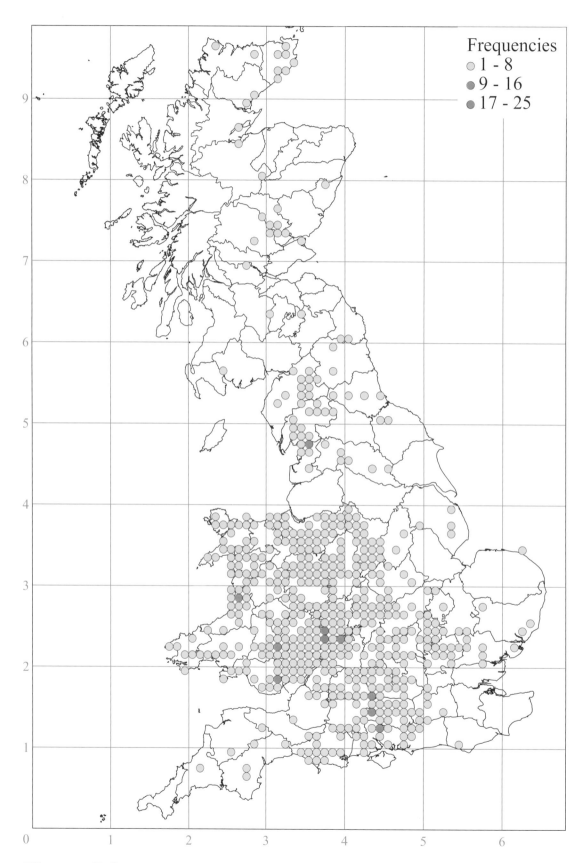

Figure 5.2 Geographical variation in the abundance of polecat and polecat-ferret records received from 10km squares during 2004-2006.

'A' class roads and the abundance of polecat records received per 10km square; Birks, 1999a). This probable effect is also apparent in parts of England: for example, the cluster of ten 'blank' 10km squares in south Shropshire is most likely to reflect the low density of 'A' roads in this area rather than an absence of polecats.

Further, the polecat is a much more familiar sight to observers in Wales than it is in England, where the species is viewed as an interesting new re-colonist in many areas; this difference in interest levels is likely to reduce the flow of polecat records reported from Wales relative to England. However, if polecats remain well-established in Wales, one would expect this to be reflected in at least some areas with higher levels of interest and recording effort. Perhaps significantly in this context, the 10km square in Wales generating most records, SN68, contains a Countryside Council for Wales (CCW) regional office and a substantial student population attached to the University of Aberystwyth. Further north, pro-active recording by members of the Snowdonia Mammal Group helped to increase the number and range of records received.

5.3 Verification of records

Table 5.1 indicates that 908 records (71.3%) were verifiable on the basis of visual inspection by the VWT; the identity of a further 22 records was confirmed via assessment by reliable contacts, making a total of 930 (73.1%) verifiable. This compares with 43.9% verifiable records during the VWT's 1990s polecat survey. All verifiable records included in Table 5.1 comprised specimens from the *Mustela putorius* or *M. furo* group. An additional two verifiable records involved specimens outwith the mustelid *putorius/ furo* group; both these were feral mink and were excluded from the database containing the remaining 1,273 records. This 'general public' misidentification rate of just 0.2% is encouraging; it gives us some confidence that the remaining unverifiable records very probably involved specimens from the *putorius/furo* group rather than other mustelids.

5.4 Phenotypic variation

5.4.1 The relative abundance of true polecats and polecat-ferrets

The 930 verifiable records were initially categorised as 'true polecat' or 'polecat-ferret' as described in section 4.5. The numbers of these two forms and the proportions of true polecats recorded from each of the countries of Great Britain are shown in Table 5.2. Plate 1 shows examples of pelage variation among the main forms encountered. The proportion of verifiably true polecats differed significantly between the three countries, (Chi-square= 55.77, *df*=5, *p*<0.001), being highest in Wales (the historical stronghold of the polecat in Britain) and lowest in Scotland (the only country of the three believed probably to have lost the polecat from its fauna in the early 20th century). These proportional data are shown for each vice-county in Appendix 3. Overall, true polecats

Table 5.2 The occurrence of verifiable polecat and polecat-ferret records received by the VWT from England, Scotland and Wales, 2004-2006.

Country	True Polecats	Polecat-ferrets	Total	% True Polecats
England	572	104	676	84.6
Scotland	9	13	22	40.9
Wales	221	11	232	95.3
Total	**802**	**128**	**930**	**86.2**

comprised 86.2% of verifiable records of the *putorius/furo* group. In terms of the density of records received, in comparison with polecats, polecat-ferrets were recorded from more than three times fewer 10km squares and at a lower density in those squares where they occurred (see sections 5.4.2 and 5.4.3 below).

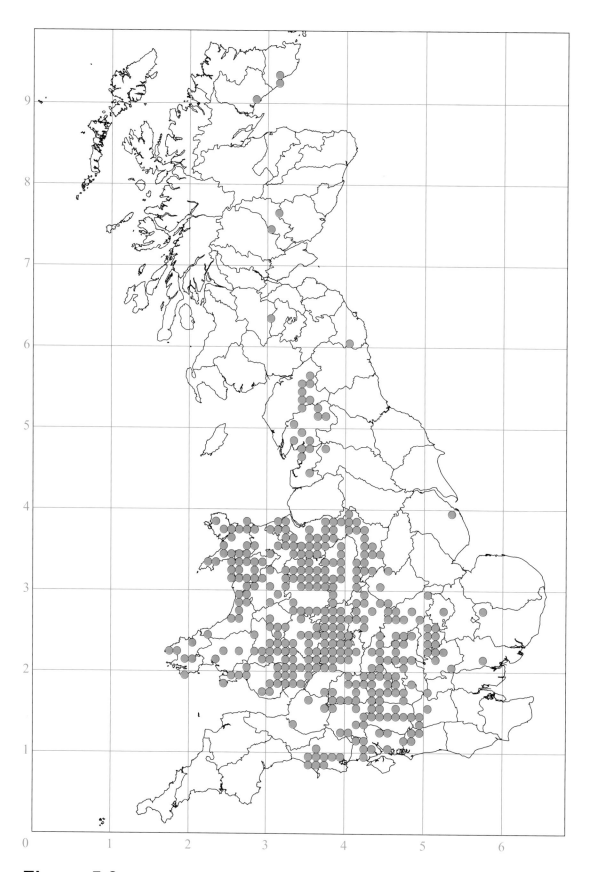

Figure 5.3   The 368 10km squares that generated verifiable records of true polecats during 2004-2006.

5.4.2 The geographical distribution of true polecats

The 802 verifiable records of true polecats were spread across 368 10km squares (a mean density of 2.2 records per occupied 10km square), as shown in Figure 5.3. This indicates a distribution based mainly in Wales, the West Midlands including Cheshire and

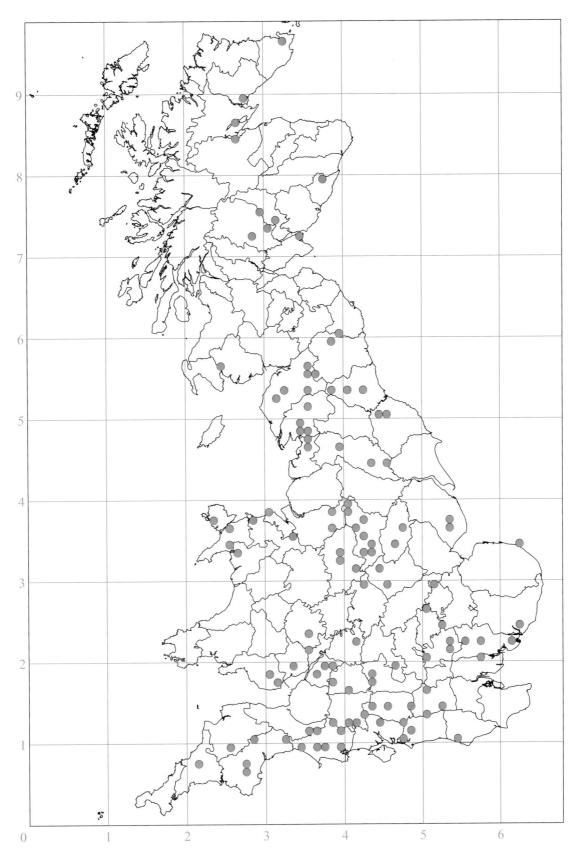

Figure 5.4 The 114 10km squares that generated verifiable records of polecat-ferrets during 2004-2006.

Derbyshire, the southern East Midlands and central southern England, with a significant outlier in Cumbria and Lancashire. More isolated records were present beyond these zones, notably in northern Scotland (VCs 107 and 110) and Perthshire. Where solitary records occur from well outside the polecat's main range, the present status of any population in that area is questionable because individual specimens might have had a captive origin. The polecat's present distribution is compared with earlier ones from the 20th century in sections 5.6 and 5.7 below.

5.4.3 The geographical distribution of polecat-ferrets

The 128 verifiable records of polecat-ferrets were spread across 114 10km squares (a mean density of 1.1 records per occupied 10km square), as shown in Figure 5.4. These records were widely distributed in Britain at a low density, though no polecat-ferret records were received from large areas of Scotland, Wales and the Marches.

5.4.4 The geographical co-occurrence of polecats and polecat-ferrets

Using the multi-species mapping facility in DMAP, it is possible to examine the extent of sympatry in polecats and polecat-ferrets. These data are summarised in Table 5.3 at two spatial scales; mapping at the 25 x 25km square scale illustrates most clearly the geographical patterns of separation and sympatry among polecats and polecat-ferrets on mainland Britain. Figure 5.5 reveals substantial areas of sympatry, with the main zones of overlap in North-west England, North Wales, the North Midlands, East Midlands, South-east Wales and central southern England. A 'polecats only' zone is apparent over much of Wales, the Welsh Marches and the central English Midlands. Areas with only polecat-ferrets present tended to occur beyond the periphery of the overlap zone, in South-west, eastern and North-east England, and in Scotland. The definition of 'Polecat Purity Zones' on the basis of varying proportions of true polecats and polecat-ferrets is considered in section 5.4.7 below.

Table 5.3 The number of recording units containing verifiable polecat and polecat-ferret records during 2004-2006, showing the extent of sympatry of these forms at two spatial scales.

Spatial scale	True polecats only	Polecat-ferrets only	Both forms present	Total
25 x 25km	87 (48.6%)	38 (21.2%)	54 (30.2%)	179
10 x 10km	325 (74.0%)	71 (16.2%)	43 (9.8%)	439

Table 5.4 The occurrence of two categories of verifiable polecat-ferret records received by the VWT from England, Scotland and Wales, 2004-2006

Country	'Dark' polecat-ferrets	'Pale' polecat-ferrets	Total	% 'Dark' polecat-ferrets
England	58	46	104	55.8
Scotland	5	8	13	38.5
Wales	7	4	11	63.6
Total	**70**	**58**	**128**	54.7

5.4.5 Proportions of 'Dark' and 'Pale' polecat-ferrets

Among the 128 verifiable polecat-ferret records received, approximately half (54.7%) were 'Dark' in pelage terms and close in appearance to true polecats and consequently challenging for recorders to recognise as polecat-ferrets. Typically these polecat-like

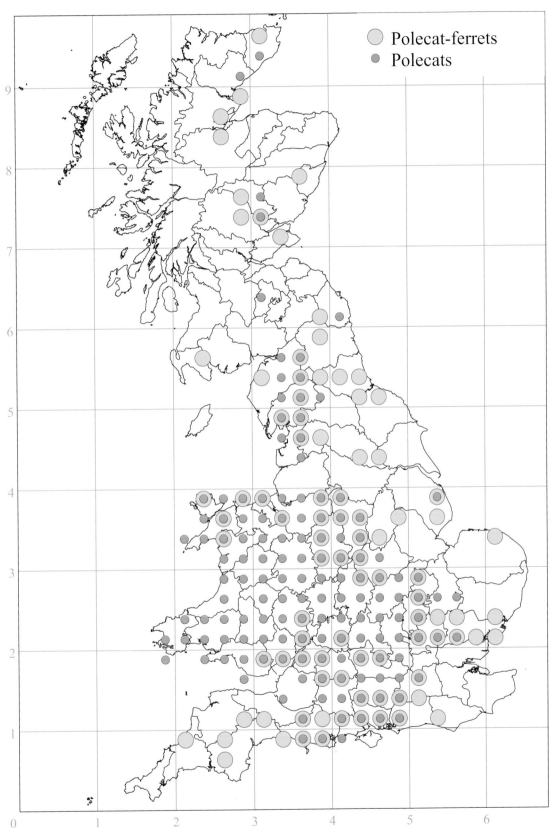

Figure 5.5 The distribution during 2004-2006 of 25 x 25km squares that generated verifiable records of true polecats only, polecat-ferrets only, and squares in which both forms occurred (see also Table 5.3).

specimens exhibited only one or two of the polecat-ferret pelage characters listed as 2, 4, 5 and 6 in Table 4.2. Table 5.4 shows that broad geographical variation in the proportions of 'Dark' and 'Pale' polecat-ferrets reflected that of the primary distinction between true polecats and polecat-ferrets shown in Table 5.2; thus, the proportion of 'Dark' polecat-ferrets was greatest in Wales and lowest in Scotland, though these differences were not statistically significant (Chi-square=1.77, df=5, p>0.05).

5.4.6 Other colour morphs

Three erythristic polecats were recorded during this survey and their details are shown in Table 5.5. This compares with two definite erythristic polecat records received during the VWT polecat survey during the 1990s, both of which were recovered as road traffic casualties (RTCs) from VC 23 (Oxford) in 1997, and fragments of a further probable erythristic specimen recovered as a RTC from VC 44 (Carmarthen) in 1995. This recessive colour morph is apparently scarce in Britain, but is clearly not restricted to one particular area.

No albino specimens were recorded during this survey, though this may be because recorders assumed any albinos were ferrets and were therefore not worth reporting.

5.4.7 Defining 'Polecat Purity Zones' in Britain

Significant inter-country differences in the proportion of polecats and polecat-ferrets (shown in Table 5.2) and evidence of substantial sympatry (Figure 5.5) warrant closer analysis in order to detect any regional patterns in their relative abundance that might be of significance to polecat conservation. Three 'Polecat Purity Zones' (PPZs) are defined in Figure 5.6, based on the proportion of phenotypically true polecats among verifiable records from individual vice-counties (using the raw data from Appendix 3). Further details of these zones are provided in Table 5.6.

The three PPZs shown in Figure 5.6 are characterised as follows:

● **PPZ 1 – Most Pure.** The 16 vice-counties comprising PPZ 1, characterised by the 'purest' polecat populations (those in which >95% of verifiable records were true polecats, shown as dark green in Figure 5.6, with further details given in Table 5.6), were concentrated mainly in Wales and the English West Midlands. This area corresponds closely to that labelled as the polecat's 'historical core' range (Birks *et al.*, 1999), comprising those vice-counties in which the polecat persisted at and beyond its distributional nadir in the early 1900s. However, an outlier cluster of three 'purest' vice-counties (Northampton, Oxford and Bucks) occurred further east. Here, 73 verifiable records included just three polecat-ferrets. Only seven verifiable polecat-ferrets were recorded over the whole of PPZ 1, and most of these were 'dark' (Table 5.6).

Table 5.5 Records of erythristic polecats received by the VWT, 2004-2006

VWT ref. no.	Date	Record type	Verification	10km square	Vice-county
1865	15/2/04	Road traffic casualty	Specimen examined by VWT	SJ57	Chester
1982	18/2/06	Road traffic casualty	Specimen examined by VWT	SO25	Radnor
2414	19/9/06	Road traffic casualty	Photo examined by VWT	SN92	Brecon

● **PPZ 2 – Intermediate Purity.** The 11 vice-counties comprising PPZ 2, characterised by polecat populations of intermediate purity (85-95% of verifiable records were

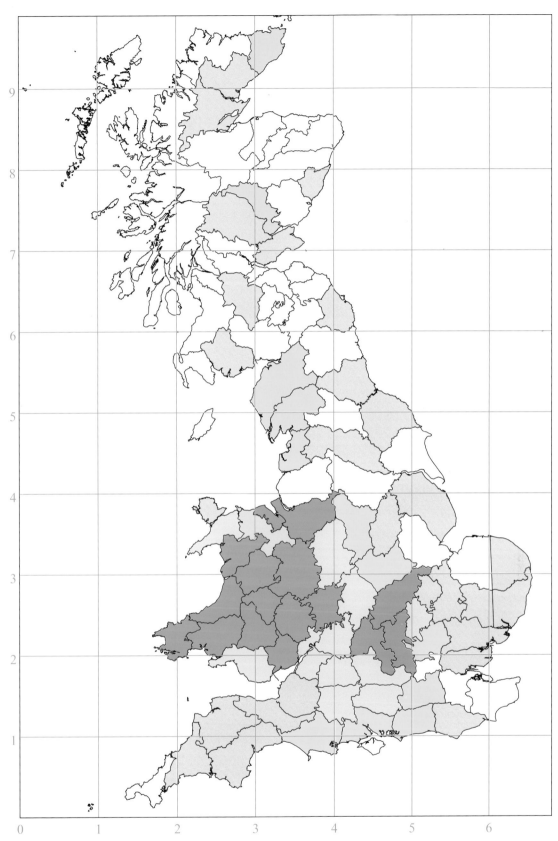

Figure 5.6 Three 'Polecat Purity Zones' (PPZs) defined on the basis of individual vice-counties in which true polecats comprised >95% (dark green = PPZ 1), 85-95% (pale green = PPZ 2) and <85% (yellow = PPZ 3) of verifiable records during 2004-2006. Vice-counties producing very few (<5) verifiable records of polecats or polecat-ferrets are shown in grey.

23

true polecats, shown as pale green in Figure 5.6, with further details in Table 5.6), were located mainly in the English Midlands and central southern England, with two in Wales (Caernarvon and Glamorgan) and one in the East Midlands (Bedford). Three of these 'intermediate' vice-counties lay between the main PPZ 1 block and the PPZ 1 eastern outlier; they were characterised by verifiable records among which polecat-ferrets were relatively scarce (just five among 57 verifiable records), comprising Warwick (94.4% true polecats), West Gloucester (87.0%) and East Gloucester (93.8%). Among the three zones, PPZ 2 had the lowest proportion of 'dark' specimens among its polecat-ferrets (Table 5.6).

- **PPZ 3 – Least Pure.** The 13 vice-counties comprising PPZ 3, characterised by the least pure polecat populations (<85% of verifiable records were true polecats, shown as yellow in Figure 5.6, with further details in Table 5.6), were mainly located around the eastern and southern periphery of the polecat's British range (e.g. VCs Derby, Leicester, Herts, Surrey, West Sussex, South Hants and Dorset), with northern outliers in North-west England (VCs West Lancs, Westmorland and Cumberland) and Scotland (VCs East Perth and Caithness); only one PPZ 3 vice-county occurred in Wales (Denbigh).

Unsurprisingly, given the criteria used to define them, the proportions of polecats and polecat-ferrets differed significantly across the three zones (Chi-square=105.9, df=5, $p<0.001$). This pattern of zonation reflects the recent eastward recolonisation of England by polecats, and their increasing tendency to reproduce with ferrets towards the fringes of the species' range. This introgression also explained the broadly comparable

Table 5.6 Characteristics of the three 'Polecat Purity Zones' (PPZs), defined on the basis of verifiable records received during 2004-2006 and illustrated in Figure 5.6

PPZ	No. of verifiable records	% true polecats overall	Constituent vice-counties	No. 'dark polecat-ferrets'	No. 'pale polecat-ferrets'
1 (16 VCs)	424	98.3	Oxford, Bucks, Northampton, Monmouth, Hereford, Worcester, Salop, Brecon, Radnor, Carmarthen, Pembroke, Cardigan, Montgomery, Merioneth, Flint, Chester	5 (71.4%)	2 (28.6%)
2 (11 VCs)	256	90.2	North Wilts, South Wilts, North Hants, Berks, Bedford, West Gloucester, East Gloucester, Warwick, Stafford, Glamorgan, Caernarvon	13 (52%)	12 (48%)
3 (13 VCs)	194	71.6	Dorset, South Hants, West Sussex, Surrey, Herts, Denbigh, Leicester, Derby, West Lancs, Westmorland, Cumberland, East Perth, Caithness	39 (70.9%)	16 (29.1%)

geographical trend in Pelage Character Totals (PCTs) reported by Kitchener *et al.* (1999), in which specimens from Wales and the Marches had more polecat-like pelage than did populations from further east.

The vice-counties coloured grey in Figure 5.6 generated too few verifiable records (<5) during the survey period to confirm that a population of polecats or polecat-ferrets was fully established. However, these included Anglesey which, according to Birks and Kitchener (1999a), had a re-establishing polecat population following the first reported recent record from 1996. With polecats able to reach the island via the Menai Bridge from the mainland of North Wales, this vice-county is well placed to be fully recolonised in the near future, but the paucity of records during 2004-2006 suggests that this process is happening slowly.

5.5 The origin of records received

Though this survey chose to focus upon road traffic casualties as the main source of records, many records were received from other sources; some of these offer insights into polecat behaviour and into the interactions between polecats and people. Table 5.7 shows the main categories of records received and the proportions of each that were verifiable. Further details of these record categories are presented in the sections below.

5.5.1 Road traffic casualties

In keeping with previous polecat distribution surveys, RTCs dominated the records received. This was inevitable in a survey organised with a particular focus on collecting visual evidence of specimens from this notoriously abundant source. Because of the ready availability of carcasses, or photographs of same, 80% of RTCs were verifiable (Table 5.7). The geographical distribution of these records, shown in Figure 5.7, reveals the influence of the road network in parts of England and Wales.

Monthly trends in the abundance of polecat RTCs, shown in Figures 5.8. and 5.9 with polecat-ferret data for comparison, reflect a seasonal pattern reported by earlier authors: after a mid-winter low, a spring (mating season) peak is followed by an early summer dip and an autumn peak (corresponding with juvenile dispersal) that typically matches or exceeds the spring peak. However, in marked contrast to the polecat trend in each of the three years, the polecat-ferret RTC trend shows a spring peak but no autumn peak. As a consequence, during this survey polecats dominated polecat-ferrets in the RTC figures to a much greater extent in the autumn (>20-fold) than they did in the spring (>3-fold).

Table 5.7 The relative occurrence of six categories of possible polecat records received by the VWT, 2004-2006, showing the proportion that were verifiable on the basis of visual evidence

Record origin	Number of records (%)		% records verifiable
Road Traffic Casualty	980	(77.0)	80.6
Live Sighting	199	(14.1)	31.7
Trapped	69	(5.4)	81.2
Unknown	4	(0.3)	100.0
Dead in Farmyard	3	(0.2)	66.6
Miscellaneous	18	(1.4)	83.3
Total	**1273**		

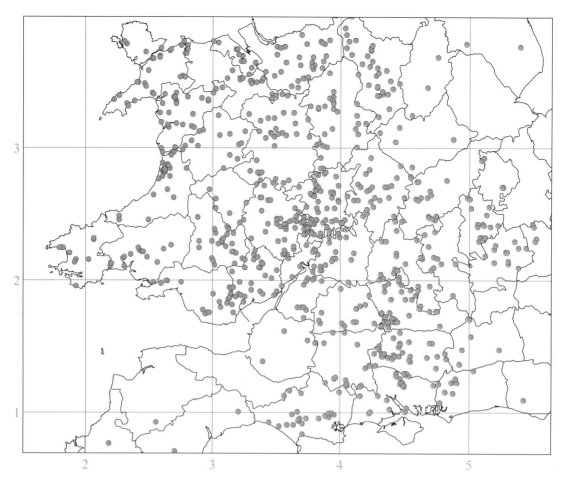

Figure 5.7 The distribution of records of RTC polecats and polecat-ferrets received during 2004-2006 from the polecat's main range in England and Wales.

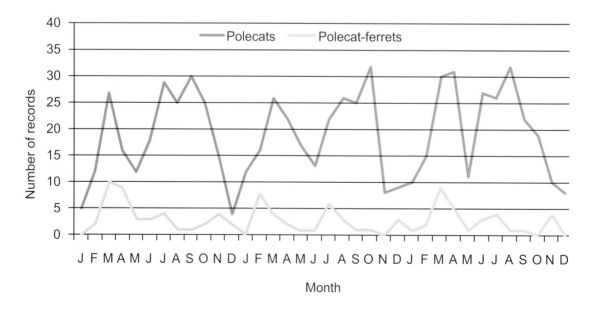

Figure 5.8 Trends in the number of verifiable RTC records of polecats (n=687) and polecat-ferrets (n=102) over the 36 months of the 2004-2006 survey.

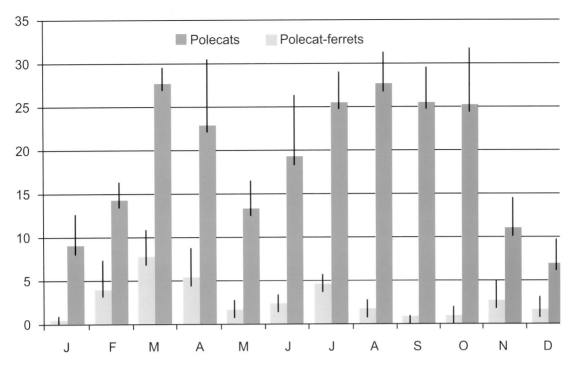

Figure 5.9 Mean values for the number of verifiable records of RTC polecats and polecat-ferrets received for each month of the 2004-2006 survey.

Differences in the occurrence of RTCs between polecats and polecat-ferrets are explored in Table 5.8 by comparing RTC numbers between spring (February to April) and autumn (August to October). These differed significantly between the two forms in two of the three survey years and over the three years combined. This suggests the existence of a behavioural difference between polecats and polecat-ferrets that, following spring mating season peaks in both forms, leads to an under-representation of polecat-ferrets among the autumn RTC sample.

5.5.2 Sightings of live polecats

Live sightings of possible polecats were common, though less than one third of these could be verified (Table 5.7) due to the understandable difficulties involved in providing visual evidence. The commonest source of live sighting records comprised polecats on roads, though many polecats were also reported from gardens and other locations (Table 5.9).

Table 5.8 A comparison of the spring : autumn ratios of verifiable RTC polecats and polecat-ferrets recorded during the 2004-2006 survey (spring = February – April; autumn = August – October).

Survey Year	No. RTC Polecats		No. RTC Polecat-ferrets		Chi square and *P* values
	Spring	**Autumn**	**Spring**	**Autumn**	
2004	55	80	21	4	15.935; <0.01
2005	64	83	14	5	6.13; >0.05
2006	76	73	16	2	9.31; <0.05
Totals	**195**	**236**	**51**	**11**	**29.69; <0.001**

Plate 1. Pelage colour variation among specimens reported to the VWT during the 2004-2006 survey:

a) *male polecat in summer pelage released after it broke in to the ferret enclosure at a Wildlife Park, Ashurst, Hants, June 2005; photo by Lynda Barton; VWT ref. 1630.*

b) *male polecat in winter pelage, showing more extensive pale frontal band; live-trapped and released during polecat study, Merioneth, 2.4.2004; photo by Kate Williamson; VWT ref. 1282.*

c) *'dark' polecat-ferret (female) showing white fur above the rhinarium and white patch on chest; specimen recovered from Enderby, Leicestershire in August 2006 and treated for back injury by Sleaford Ferret Rescue; note defensive posture and 'bottle-brush' tail indicating wild origin; photo by Julie Stoodley; VWT ref. 2316.*

d) *'dark' polecat-ferret trapped accidentally in rabbit trap at Potten End, Herts. on 20.9.2006 and released; note pinkish rhinarium not normally found in true polecats; photo by Mr & Mrs Haworth; VWT ref. 2392*

e) *'pale' polecat-ferret recorded on 2.5.2006 at Tregarth, Bangor; photo by Nigel Beidas; VWT ref. 2130.*

f) *Tame adult male polecat in summer pelage ('Deezel') recovered as an orphan kit from Gateley in North Hants in 2005 and hand-reared; photo on 30.5.2006 by JDSB; VWT ref. 2523.*

Plate 2.   Polecats seen in gardens, houses and out-houses, 2004-2006:

a) adult polecat (with metal alien) in Hale, Cheshire, 5.9.04; photo by John Richards; VWT ref, 1407;

b) polecat kits born under decking in a garden in Kidderminster, Worcs.; photo by Ann Robinson, 17.7.06; VWT ref 2225;

c) one of three polecats found living in a garage in Madeley, Shropshire; owners fed family on ferret food; photo Phil Wilson, 3.8.06; VWT ref 2265;

d) 'Mineem', an orphaned wild polecat reared 'free range' in 2005 at a house near Ruardean, Glos., which left then returned to give birth beneath the house in 2006; photo Andrew Anderson, July 2005; VWT ref. 2167;

e) Polecat live-trapped accidentally in rabbit trap (and released) in a garden at Dry Sandford, Oxon in August 2006. Note defensive threat posture. Photo by Ros & Steve Grigson; VWT ref. 2261.

f) adult polecat cornered in old duck house, Llanover, Monmouthshire, 19.7.05; photo by Paula Francis; VWT ref. 1670.

Plate 3.   Polecats seen on roads 2004-2006:

a)

b)

c)

d)

a) - d) A series of photographs of a polecat family group (mother with six young) on a minor road on Swallowcliffe Down, Wiltshire at 14:30h on 20.6.06. Photographs by Simon Edwards (taken through vehicle windscreen); VWT ref.2172;

e) live polecat at night at a roadside burrow near Bincombe, Dorset, 30.9.04; photo by Lynda Wakelin; VWT ref.1520.

Table 5.9 The relative occurrence across the three countries of three categories of 'Live Sighting' polecat or polecat-ferret records received by the VWT, 2004-2006

Record category	England	Scotland	Wales	Total (%)	10km squares
Live sighting (house or garden)	51	2	15	68 (34.2)	58
Live sighting (road)	63	2	17	82 (41.2)	68
Live sighting (other)	37	3	9	49 (24.6)	48
Total	**151**	**7**	**41**	**199 (100)**	**152**

5.5.2.1 Polecats in gardens

Of the 68 live sightings of possible polecats in gardens, 25 (36.7%) were supported by visual evidence (21 still photographs, three video clips and one live specimen examined). This evidence, together with descriptions of encounters supplied by observers (see Appendix 4), was helpful in judging whether the animals were likely to be wild polecats or polecat-ferrets of wild or domestic origin. Plate 2 shows examples of polecats photographed in houses and gardens during the survey. Of the 25 verifiable records, eight (32%) were classed as polecat-ferrets on the basis of pelage colour (only one of these was a 'pale' polecat-ferret). This proportion of polecat-ferrets is higher than that found among verifiable records over the survey as a whole (13.8%; see Table 4.2). Further, the 'tame' behaviour of some animals observed in gardens, regardless of pelage colour, suggested a recent captive origin (Appendix 4). Nevertheless, the appearance and reported behaviour of many animals seen in gardens were typical of true wild polecats: some of this involved polecat families, usually comprising a mother and young that occupied dens in gardens associated with decking or outbuildings; some reports involved successful predation of wild prey or consumption of a variety of food put out for wild or domestic animals (Appendix 4, summarised in Table 5.10). The time of day or night was specified in 24 reported sightings of possible polecats in gardens; these fell equally between 'night-time' (19:00-06:59h BST) and daytime (07:00-18:59h BST) sightings.

Table 5.10 The occurrence of non-exclusive categories of behaviour shown in gardens by possible polecats, reported to the VWT during 2004-2006 (information summarised from Appendix 4)

Reported activities of possible polecats seen in gardens	Number of cases reported
Successful predation of wild rabbit (3), frog (2), blackbird (1)	6
Attempted predation of pets or poultry	2
Eating food put out for cats, foxes, hedgehogs (or polecats)	13
General foraging	4
Presence of polecat family	18
Polecat(s) living in or beneath shed/garage/conservatory/henhouse	11
Polecat(s) living beneath decking	6
Playing	4
Entered house through catflap or other gap	5

Polecats reported as taking food in gardens apparently showed a preference for fresh meat or fish over dried foods. Where suitable food was left out in the open, typically a polecat would appear after dark, quickly collect an item of food and rush to cover to consume it. Clark (2006) describes such behaviour reported from a garden at Tewin in Hertfordshire during the survey period (and see Appendix 4).

Sightings of possible polecats in gardens were markedly concentrated in late summer (Chi-square = 52.97, df = 11, $p<0.001$), with 63% occurring in just three months (July-September; see Figures 5.10 and 5.11). Figure 5.10 suggests that the occurrence of possible polecats in gardens increased sharply over the three survey years, though this pattern is more likely explained in terms of increased awareness of the survey as it progressed.

Reports of possible garden polecats were received from 26 vice-counties (Appendix

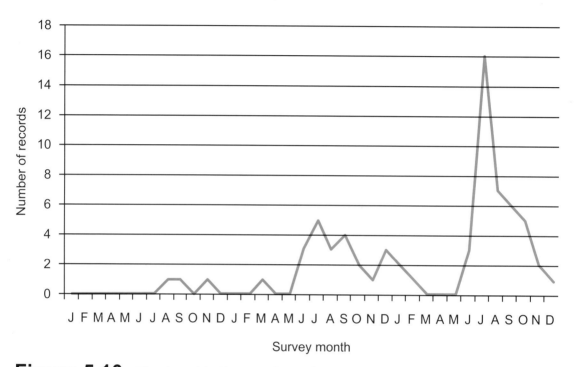

Figure 5.10 The trend in the number of reports of possible polecats (n=68) seen in gardens over the 36 months of the 2004-2006 survey.

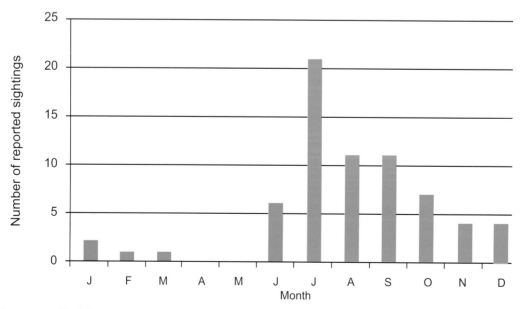

Figure 5.11 Total numbers of reports of possible garden polecats (n=68) seen per month over the 2004-2006 survey, with data from all three years combined.

4), though 37 reports (54.4%) came from just five VCs: Chester (12 records), Salop (8), Stafford (6), Worcester (6, of which 3 from the Kidderminster area) and Glamorgan (5). It is notable that these five VCs comprised three in PPZ 1 and two from PPZ 2 as defined in Section 5.4.7. Several reports of polecats in gardens were from urban areas: for example, the Chester VC records were largely concentrated around the fringes of south Manchester (4 records from Hale, Hazel Grove and Wilmslow) and in Macclesfield (4). During the survey, Cheshire Wildlife Trust received many separate reports of garden polecats that are not included in the data presented here (Sue Tatman pers. comm.). These included a litter of polecats born and raised in a cellar, a polecat drowned in a swimming pool and one rescued from a water cistern.

Among the 68 reports of possible polecats in gardens, four included expressions of concern from householders about possible adverse impacts: two related to unspecified worries about possible 'damage'; one involved concerns about a possible threat to children; one involved concerns about the safety of fish in a garden pond. Most observers, however, appeared pleased to have had encounters with polecats in their gardens.

Further interactions between people and polecats in gardens are described in the section on trapped animals (Section 5.5.3 below).

5.5.2.2 Polecats on roads

Over the 2004-2006 survey period, the VWT received 82 reports of live polecats or polecat-ferrets seen on or beside roads. Many of these reports included descriptions of behaviour, summarised in Table 5.11, that go some way towards explaining the polecat's particular vulnerability to road traffic: road corridors are clearly used by polecats for foraging (reports included polecats chasing rabbits and feeding on fresh carrion on roads) and by breeding female polecats for moving kits around their home ranges (see Plate 3). Some of this activity occurred in daytime when the risk of vehicle collision is high.

Table 5.11 The occurrence of non-exclusive categories of activities/ observations of possible polecats seen on roads and reported to the VWT during 2004-2006

Reported activities of possible polecats seen on roads	Number of cases reported
Family group of mother and young	11
Injured or orphaned animal recovered and taken into captivity	9
Foraging for live prey or carrion	8
Crossing road	15
Playing	3

The death of breeding female polecats due to RTCs in mid-summer creates roadside orphans, some of which are found and rescued by people. The following email sent by Mr. and Mrs. Anderson to the VWT describes one such encounter and the subsequent story of 'Mineem', a young female polecat that, having become independent, chose to return the following year to give birth beneath her rescuers' house (see also Plate 2d):

" We were most interested in your appeal for sightings of polecats.
Our son was driving home about 10.00 pm last July (2005) when he saw a small animal in the road, about to get run over. This was near Ruardean, Glos. He rescued it and brought it home where we fed it and decided it might be reclaimed if we put it back. We

33

returned it to the hedge by the road verge and it made a contact call, so we hoped its family might find it. It was still there the next morning and we left food and water. We collected it in the afternoon as it was still there.

We kept it at home in a cage, though it spent periods loose in the room playing and exploring the interior of the sofa. After some months, we left its cage open outside. It later appeared at a mouse hole under the corner of a ground floor extension. We enlarged the hole so she could come up, keeping a brick over the hole. Over last winter we would hear her scratch and let her in. She would hide under furniture, coming out to collect day-old chicks or best mince. She would disappear for 2 or 3 days at a time. Last February or March she was having difficulty getting up the hole. After she had taken down tissues and pillow stuffing down, we heard young squeaking. We replaced the brick over her hole with a cage top, so we could leave food and water that she was free to come up for. The young came up when older, though mother was always dragging them down again. We opened the cage so they could venture into the room. We don't know how many there were. We never saw more than two at a time.

The last day they were here there were several under the furniture making contact calls. It was getting difficult to tell them from their mother. They all left about 3 weeks ago. We have not seen them since."

Several roadside orphan polecats were passed to the RSPCA's wildlife hospital at Stapeley Grange in Cheshire. There, staff have established expertise in retaining the wary nature of young polecats so as to maximise the success of subsequent releases into the wild.

5.5.3 Trapped animals

Polecats commonly enter traps set for other species. During the survey the VWT received 69 reports of possible polecats caught in traps (some reports involved several animals trapped separately over a period of days or weeks) and most of these reports were verifiable (Table 5.7), usually on the basis of photographs; ten were categorised as polecat-ferrets (six 'dark' and four 'pale'), indicating that true polecats comprised over 80% of all animals trapped. In 58 cases animals were reportedly released unharmed from cage traps (Table 5.12) and 12 of these involved animals trapped in gardens, outbuildings or, in one case, in a squirrel trap set in a house roof. The seasonal pattern of reports of trapped polecats broadly matched that revealed by road casualties (Figure 5.12).

Eleven cases involved animals that were either killed deliberately after being caught in cage traps or died from injuries sustained in spring traps set in tunnels (so-called 'tunnel traps'). This lethal trapping category is probably under-represented in this survey because of uncertainties about the legality of killing polecats in traps and a reluctance to report such incidents to a conservation organisation. Cases of polecats injured or killed

Table 5.12 The occurrence of possible polecats released unharmed from cage traps and reported to the VWT during 2004-2006

Category of trapping	Number of animals
Caught in cage trap set for rabbits	14
Caught in cage trap as part of mink control operations	11
Caught in cage trap during research on polecats or mink	6
Caught in cage trap set for squirrels	4
Caught in cage trap set for foxes	2
Caught in cage trap set for rats	2

in spring traps were typically reported by members of the public who had encountered the animals by chance: in one case (in North Hants) a polecat was found dead in a field having apparently dragged itself from a nearby wood with a spring trap attached; in another (in Hertfordshire), a live polecat with a spring trap attached to a forelimb was found and photographed by a member of the public; the animal was later killed by the trapper; the police and RSPCA were contacted but no action was taken.

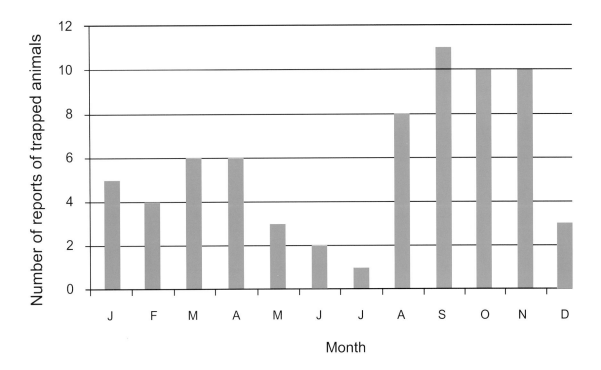

Figure 5.12 Monthly variation in reports of possible polecats trapped in Britain (n=69) during the 2004-2006 survey, with data from all three years combined.

5.5.4 Other records

A further 25 records of possible polecats were received, comprising seven animals found dead away from roads or farmyards; three found dead or dying in farmyards (and, therefore, believed possibly to be victims of secondary rodenticide poisoning); three killed by dogs; four of unknown origin; one recovered as a very young kit and hand-reared; one shot; and one killed by a lynx at a wildlife park in Cardiganshire (curiously, during the VWT's 1990s polecat survey, a polecat was killed by a leopard at a wildlife park in Oxfordshire).

5.6 Changes in polecat distribution since the mid-twentieth century

Figure 5.13 shows, in terms of changes in numbers of occupied 10km squares, how the polecat's distributional range in Britain has expanded since organised distribution-mapping was started by Walton (1964) in 1959. Authors of successive distribution surveys in this series have tended to adopt a cumulative approach, involving assumptions that 10km squares recorded as positive by previous surveyors remained positive in the latest one. A period of relatively passive and conservative recording in the 1980s and early 1990s, followed by more active 'catch-up' recording during the VWT's 1990s survey (explained by Birks, 1999a) is apparent in Figure 5.13. Such changes in the recorded rate of accretion to the polecat's expanding range are explored in Figure 5.14, which shows the percentage increase in range between surveys and the mean number of 10km squares added per year between surveys (the latter is useful because inter-survey intervals vary between three to nine years, with a mean

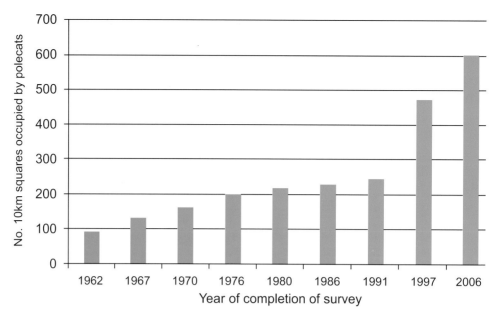

Figure 5.13 Changes in the cumulative number of 10km squares recorded as occupied by polecats in Britain since organised distribution-mapping was initiated. In chronological order, the data for each bar are from Walton (1964), Walton (1968), Corbet (1971), Arnold (1978), Teall (1982), Blandford (1987), Arnold (1993), Birks (1999a) and the present survey. Note that the authors of each successive survey have tended to adopt a cumulative approach to polecat distribution; data from Arnold (1984) are omitted from this figure because such an approach was not fully adopted so the distribution appeared to contract.

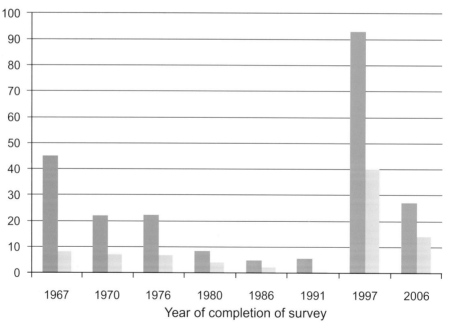

Figure 5.14 Accretion of new areas to the polecat's range between distribution surveys in Britain shown as the percentage increase in the number of occupied 10km squares since the previous survey (dark bars) and the mean number of 10km squares added per year since the previous survey (pale bars). Note that the 1997 survey involved substantial 'catch-up' recording that explains the peak in both parameters (see section 5.6). Survey authors are shown in the legend of Figure 5.13.

of 4.89 years). Only over the last two inter-survey intervals did the accretion rate exceed ten new 10km squares per year, with the greatest rate achieved by Birks's (1999a) 'catch-up' survey that followed a period of relatively conservative recording. The present survey recorded an accretion rate of 14.33 new 10km squares per year since the previous survey.

Table 5.13 Changes in the number of 10km squares recorded as occupied by polecats in Britain between earlier post-1950 surveys and the 2004-2006 one (1990-1997 survey data from Birks, 1999a; earlier survey data from Walton, 1964, 1968; Corbet, 1971; Arnold, 1978, 1984, 1993; Teall, 1982; Blandford, 1987).

Recording unit	No. 10km squares in which polecats recorded in 1990-1997	No. 10km squares in which verifiable polecats recorded in 2004-2006	Cumulative total occupied 10km squares 1959-2006	No. new 10km squares added in 2004-2006 to previously recorded 1959-1997 distribution
Wales	62	104	219	13
England	253	258	370	111
Scotland	8	6	14	6
Great Britain	323	368	603	130

5.7 Recent range expansion

The present survey recorded verifiable polecats in 130 10km squares from which they had not been recorded since 1950; 85% of these new squares were in England (Table 5.13), suggesting that this was the main area of recent range expansion. In Figure 5.15 comparisons are drawn between the distributions recorded by the present survey and the 1990s survey by Birks (1999a); the distribution from the present survey is compared with that from all previous post-1950 surveys in Figure 5.16. The main changes are discussed area by area in the sections below.

5.7.1 Scotland

No verifiable records were received during the present survey from Argyll, where a population was described as re-established over a minimum of eight 10km squares during the 1990s (Craik & Brown, 1997) following an earlier release. This absence of records is unlikely to be an artefact of low recording effort, because the main recorder of the 1990s population was still active in the area during the present survey and no specimens were recovered (Clive Craik, pers. comm.). It is possible that this population has become extinct, though further survey effort should be deployed to confirm whether this is the case.

Records were received from parts of Perthshire (mostly from the East Perth VC) where the VWT has been informed of the release of polecats since the early 1990s. A wild population appears now to be established in this area; however, the majority of the specimens available for examination were not true polecats (Appendix 3), so this area falls into PPZ 3 (Figure 5.6; Table 5.6). Some of these specimens are in a collection at Perth Museum (Mark Simmons, pers. comm.).

During the 1990s the VWT received reports of polecat-like specimens from Caithness (Birks, 1999a), but no specimens were then available for examination. Among several more recent reports, seven specimens from Caithness and the adjacent East Sutherland VC were examined during the present survey, and five were classed as polecats on initial inspection. A population appears to be established in this area, though its origin is uncertain. Solow *et al.* (2006) considered the alternative explanations of either long-term survival since the early 1900s or recent reintroduction and favoured the latter. However, inquiries have led to no evidence of reintroductions, so the possibility

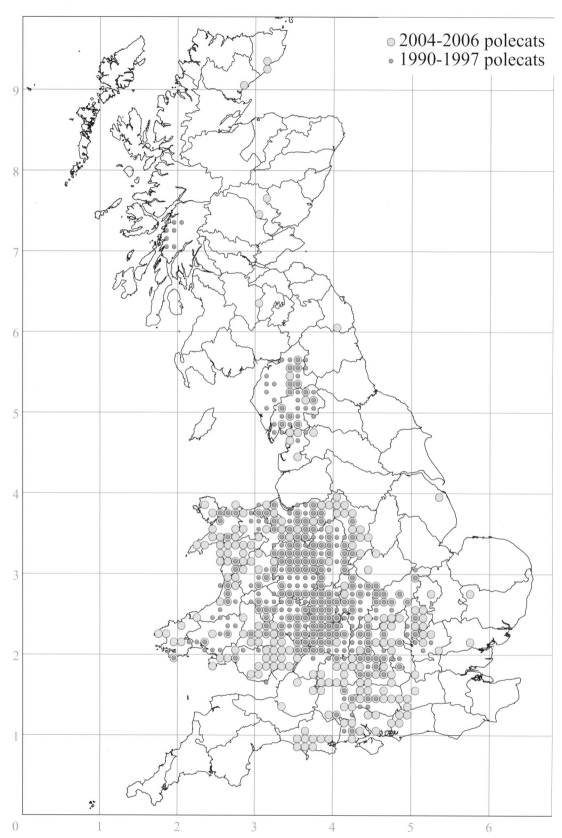

Figure 5.15 The coincidence of 10km squares recorded as occupied by polecats during the present survey (n=368) and the 1990s survey (n=323) by Birks (1999a); coincident squares are those with two symbol colours.

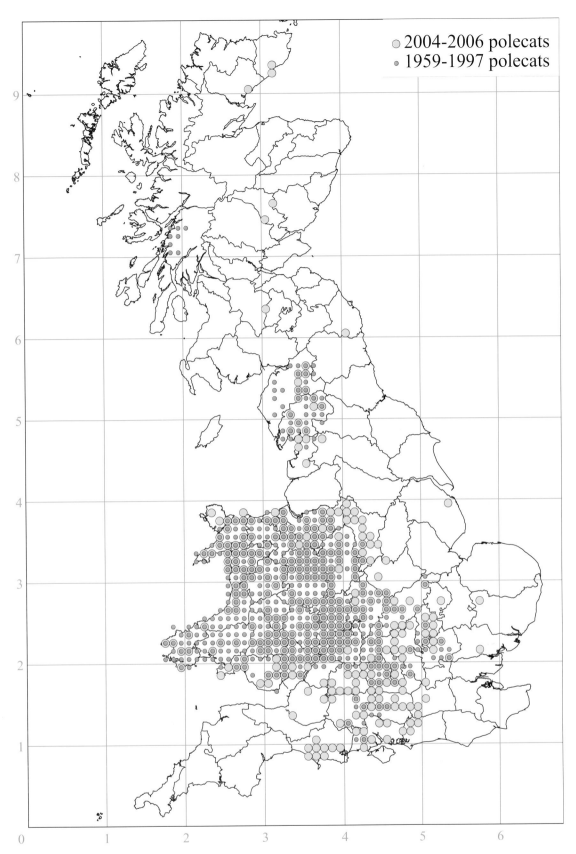

Figure 5.16 The coincidence of 10km squares recorded as occupied by polecats during the present survey (n=368) and the cumulative occurrence of occupied squares (n=473) as recorded by surveys from 1959 to 1997 (Walton, 1964, 1968; Corbet, 1971; Arnold, 1978, 1984, 1993; Teall, 1982; Blandford, 1987; Birks, 1999a); coincident squares are those with two symbol colours; newly positive squares contain yellow only symbols.

remains that polecats may have persisted undetected through the twentieth century in this area of very low human population.

Jones (1992) reported on the release of a small number of polecats on the southern side of Loch Ness in 1982 and suggested that this may have failed due to culling by gamekeepers. However, although no records were received from that area during the present survey, a report from November 2003 suggests that a polecat population may still be present near Fort Augustus (David Kent, pers. comm.).

In southern Scotland, verifiable records were received of a polecat from Lanark VC and a polecat-ferret from Kirkcudbright VC. The polecat population in Cumbria, North-west England has apparently not yet expanded northwards into southern Scotland.

5.7.2 Northern England (north of Manchester)

The population reintroduced into Cumbria since the 1970s (Birks, 1999a) clearly persists, though polecat records were less widespread during the present survey than during the 1990s (Figure 5.15). There is little evidence of expansion by this population into adjacent counties, the exception being a slight southward extension further into Lancashire. Polecat-ferrets were common in this area (Figure 5.4 and Appendix 3), so the Cumbria/Lancashire population is classed as PPZ 3 (Figure 5.6, Table 5.6).

5.7.3 Wales

The paucity of recent records from many parts of Wales is surprising, considering that the Principality provided the polecat with its main stronghold during the species' distributional nadir in the late nineteenth and early twentieth century. Table 5.13 and Figure 5.15 show that the present survey was more successful than its immediate predecessor in verifying the presence of polecats in Welsh 10km squares; nevertheless there were many squares, especially in the southern half of Wales, from which no polecats were recorded during the present survey. The possible reasons for this have already been considered in section 5.2.1. The present survey added 13 new 10km squares to the post-1950 recorded distribution in Wales, and all these were located on the northern (VCs Anglesey, Denbigh and Flint) and southern (Glamorgan and Monmouth) fringes of the Principality. If one dares to assume that the present distribution is truly reflected by the cumulative spread of records collected since 1959, and the two long-term blank squares in upland mid-Wales are artefacts of the near-absence of roads within them, the only remaining truly 'blank' areas in Wales would appear to be in the vice-counties of Glamorgan and Anglesey (Figure 5.16).

5.7.4 Central and southern England

Figures 5.15 and 5.16 indicate that the greatest recent changes in polecat distribution have occurred in central and southern England. Here, the 2004-2006 survey added many new 10km squares to the previously recorded distribution, confirming a significant recent expansion in range. The broad areas of greatest range expansion since the 1990s survey are identified in Figure 5.17 as seven vice-counties, in each of which more than five new 10km squares have been added to the polecat's distribution. It is encouraging to note that these 'expansion' VCs are not all characterised by populations of low purity (see also Figure 5.6 and Table 5.6): one (Bucks) lies in PPZ 1; three (North Wilts, Berks and North Hants) lie in PPZ 2; and three (Dorset, Derby and South Hants) lie in PPZ 3.

Despite a probable presence of polecats in Cheshire since the 1970s, there has been no significant northward expansion of the Midlands range since the 1990s survey, suggesting that the linked conurbations of Liverpool and Manchester represent a significant barrier. The main expansion in the Midlands to the north of the West Midlands conurbation has been eastward into Derbyshire.

To the south of the West Midlands conurbation, there has been significant expansion

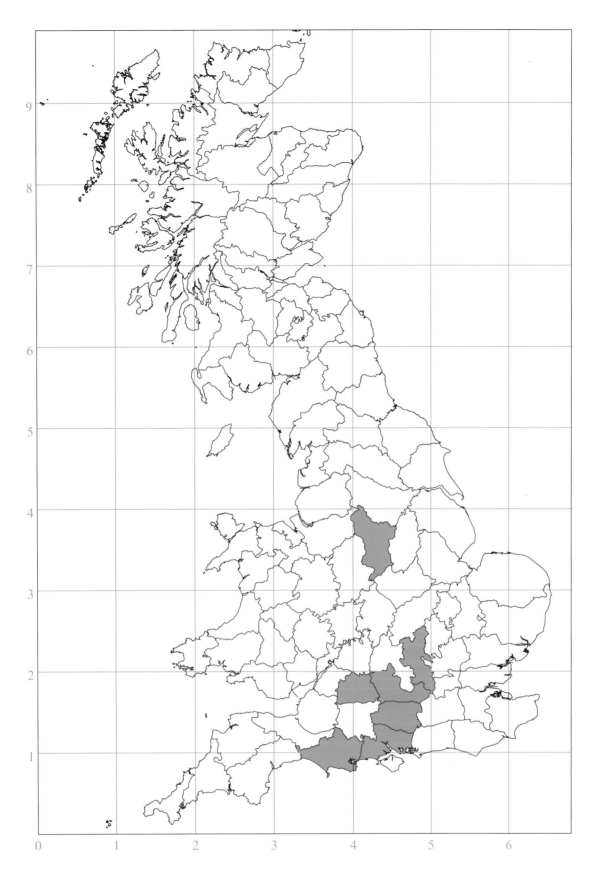

Figure 5.17 The most active areas of polecat range expansion in Britain between the 1990s survey (Birks, 1999a) and the present survey, indicated by those vice-counties in which >5 new positive 10km squares were recorded during 2004-2006: Derby, Bucks, Berks, North Wilts, Dorset, North Hants and South Hants (raw data presented in Appendix 5).

eastward into the East Midland vice-counties of Bucks, Bedford and Herts. Significantly, though some gaps remain in Bucks, this East Midlands block is now effectively contiguous with the main Midlands range; during the 1990s survey it was identified as an outlier arising from one or more reintroductions (Birks, 1999a).

Further south, as a consequence of recent range expansion, populations in central southern England identified in the 1990s as isolated and probably arising from reintroductions are now contiguous with the main English range. A population in Dorset, reported but unconfirmed in the 1990s and also of unknown origin, now appears well established and possibly contiguous with the population in South Hants to the east. This recent consolidation of the polecat's range in central southern England has led to the initial recolonisation of new vice-counties on the fringes: Surrey and West Sussex to the east; North Somerset to the west.

5.8 A 2006 population estimate for the polecat in Britain

Evidence of significant recent range expansion indicates that the British polecat population is likely to have increased since the VWT's 1990s survey. A new estimate can be produced by using the same population density figures derived from 1990s live-trapping data in the 'current core' and 'current fringe' of the polecat's range (see Birks *et al.* (1999) for an explanation of these terms and how the areas were defined): 101 polecats per 10km square was used as the winter population density estimate for the 'current core', comprising the twelve Welsh and English Marches vice-counties of Caernarvon, Denbigh, Flint, Merioneth, Montgomery, Cardigan, Radnor, Carmarthen, Brecon, Chester, Salop, and Hereford; 69 polecats per 10km square was the comparable 1990s density estimate for the 'current fringe', comprising all other vice-counties in which polecat populations had become re-established following range expansion. In the absence of more recent data on population density variation in British polecats, it was assumed that the same divisions between the 'current core' and 'current fringe' held during the present survey.

With the exception of the Argyll population in the West of Scotland that may have become extinct, it was assumed that any 10km squares recorded as occupied in previous post-1950 distribution surveys remained occupied for the purposes of this new population estimate. As in Birks *et al.*'s (1999) population estimate, occupied 10km squares containing substantial areas of sea are assumed to contain 50% of the polecats present in purely terrestrial squares. The 2006 population estimate, including separate figures for Scotland, Wales and England, is presented in Table 5.14. This suggests that the polecat population of Britain has increased by 8,403 (21.9%) at an initial rate of 934 (2.4%) per year since 1997. Almost all of this estimated increase (7,784, or 92.6%) has occurred in England.

Table 5.14 A minimum winter population estimate for the polecat in Britain in 2006, showing the 1997 estimate by Birks *et al.* (1999) for comparison; see text in Section 5.8 for explanation of calculations.

	No. 'current core' 10km squares @ 101 polecats per square	No. 'current fringe' 10km squares @ 69 polecats per square	Minimum 2006 population estimate	1997 estimate (Birks *et al.*, 1999)	% change between 1997 & 2006
Scotland	0	4 (+2 @ 50%)	345	483	-28.6
Wales	134 (+ 29 @ 50%)	44 (+12 @ 50%)	18,448	17,691	+4.3
England	78	291 (+1 @ 50%)	27,991	20,207	+38.5
GB Total	212 (+ 29 @ 50%)	339 (+15 @ 50%)	46,784	38,381	+21.9

6. DISCUSSION

The polecat's twentieth century recovery in Britain was a spark of good news to brighten the environmental doom and gloom. While its fellow nineteenth century *disparus*, the wildcat *Felis sylvestris* and pine marten *Martes martes*, still clung to north-western strongholds, the polecat crept quietly back through middle England. The present survey confirms that this encouraging trend has continued into the new millennium. Like the buzzard, its resurgent avian soul-mate, the polecat has recently returned to parts of the Home Counties from which it was exterminated over a hundred years ago. Many issues are raised by the return of this once-loathed and now little-known predator; some of the important ones are considered in the sections below: how will the polecat's recovery proceed in the future? What influence does introgression with ferrets have? How will the polecat interact with other carnivores in Britain? How will polecats and people interact as we get to know each other second time around?

It is important to place the polecat's British recovery in a wider European context. Several populations on the European continent were described as declining in the late twentieth century (reviewed by Birks & Kitchener, 1999b), and a recent study of genetic structure in continental populations reveals evidence of recent decline and advance in different parts of Europe (Pertoldi *et al.*, 2006). The sustained recovery in Britain over the past 50 or more years, is therefore, something of an exception.

6.1 The pattern of polecat recovery

The driving forces behind the polecat's recovery in Britain, principally reduced culling by humans during the first half of the twentieth century and, later, a post-myxomatosis increase in numbers of rabbits *Oryctolagus cuniculus* (a key polecat prey species), have been described by several authors and reviewed by Birks (1999a). Another critical factor that has allowed the polecat to repopulate modern landscapes is its apparent lack of specific habitat requirements, though a general preference for lowland rather than upland areas has been reported in Britain (Birks & Kitchener, 1999b, 2008) and, in southern Europe, there is evidence of a strong association with riparian habitats (Rondinini *et al.*, 2006).

Wales is now almost fully reoccupied by polecats and has been so at least since the previous survey by Birks (1999a); the exceptions are Anglesey (apparently still being recolonised following the first recent polecat record from the island in 1996) and Glamorgan (where a high density of main roads may be preventing the re-establishment of polecat populations). However, this conclusion of a near-complete reoccupation of Wales is based on the assumption, inherent in the cumulative distribution-mapping approach, that no ground has been lost there since proper surveys started in 1959. That assumption is questionable in light of the sparse spread of records from Wales during the present survey and that of Birks (1999a), even though this effect is probably explained by the low numbers of recorders and 'recorder complacency' in the polecat's Welsh heartland (see Section 5.2.1).

Are polecats still present in all the 10km squares from which they have been recorded during and since Walton's (1964) first survey? Could some decline in distribution or abundance have been concealed by the assumptions made by successive authors of distribution maps? These questions have to be faced, though some reassurance can be found in the VWT's polecat abundance monitoring data: Figure 6.1 suggests that, while polecat abundance in Wales tends to be lower than that in the West Midlands, it tends to exceed that in North-west England and the East Midlands. Nevertheless, the case for more active recording of polecats in the Principality is strong, and the cumulative approach should be resisted in future wide scale distribution-mapping exercises. A Wales-wide distribution survey seeking to confirm polecat presence in every 10km square since 1999 would be valuable.

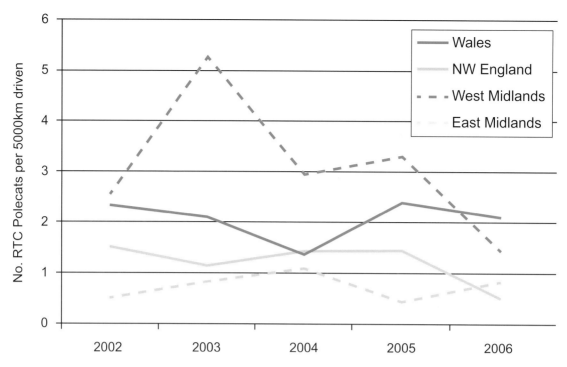

Figure 6.1 Trends in simple abundance indices for polecats for 2002-2006 in Wales and three of the English Development Agency regions; data are derived from the VWT's annual abundance monitoring exercise, involving hand-picked recorders counting numbers of RTC polecats seen against distance driven during September and October (VWT, unpublished data).

The apparent repopulation of Wales during the late twentieth century means that, if one disregards translocations to other parts of Britain, subsequent expansion of the polecat's main range could only occur through and beyond the English Midlands. The present survey confirms that this process is well under way. Early geographical constraints to range expansion imposed by the peninsular shape of Wales no longer apply. Compared with the early 1990s, the polecat's main range in England now has a much larger effective perimeter from which future expansion can occur. Therefore, while conditions remain suitable for polecats, the rate of range expansion should be increasing. Expectations of unconstrained spread may be unwise, however, if there is merit in the 'pressure gradient' concept suggested by Birks (2000). He warned that threats to polecat survival tend to increase from the sparsely populated (by humans) upland core of its range towards the expanding fringes in the densely populated lowlands.

The post-1997 mean expansion rate of 14.3 new 10km squares re-occupied per year cannot be compared directly with the rate of 40.33 new squares per year recorded by the previous survey because of its 'catch-up' recording element, in which an estimated 70% of apparent range expansion in the 1990s was accounted for by previously unrecorded reintroduced populations (38%) and pre-1991 range expansion (32%) (Birks, 1999a). However, once this 'catch-up' element is removed, the estimated natural range expansion rate in the 1990s was 12.1 (30% of 40.33) new 10km squares per year. Thus, the modest rise in annual expansion rate from 12.1 10km squares in the 1990s to 14.3 squares subsequently fits our expectations of an increasing rate.

The polecat's particular vulnerability to road traffic casualties led Birks *et al.* (1999) to suggest that areas of high traffic density could represent population sinks or dispersal barriers, to the extent that these could influence its pattern of re-establishment in Britain. By association this includes heavily built up areas and their linking transport

44

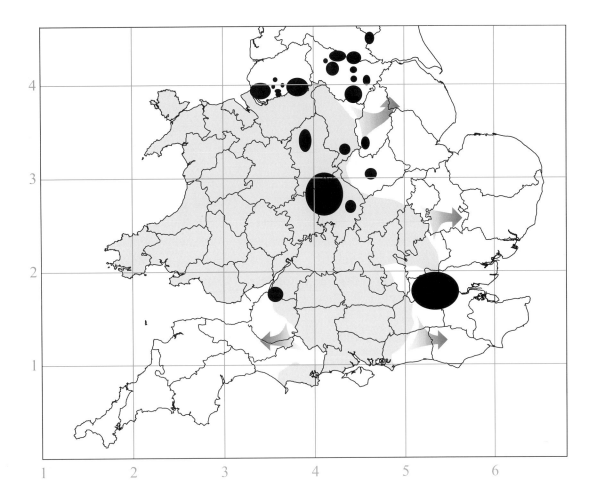

Figure 6.2 A schematic representation of the polecat's main range in England and Wales (green), showing the locations of cities and conurbations (black) of significance in influencing recent and future range expansion. Arrows represent the likely main directions of future spread.

networks, such as the Liverpool and Manchester conurbations that were identified in the present survey as a barrier to northward dispersal from the English Midlands. Figure 6.2 illustrates the distribution of such areas in relation to the polecat's main range and predictions for the pattern of future spread. Beyond the polecat's current range, further barriers are apparent in northern England: the concentration of urban areas and transport networks within an oblong from Liverpool and Preston in the west to Leeds, Doncaster and Sheffield in the east, with the Pennine uplands running through it from north to south, represents a substantial block of relatively unfavourable habitat for polecats. If this area proves to be impermeable to polecat dispersal, the only available route northward for an expanding Midlands population lies to the east of Sheffield and Doncaster.

Further south, the density of urban areas is much lower, so there have been fewer apparent constraints on polecat range expansion. The greater eastward range expansion apparent to the south of the West Midlands conurbation may be an effect of more favourable lowland habitat in the South Midlands compared with the upland character of the Peak District and Cannock Chase to the north (as suggested by Birks, 1999a); additionally, recent coalescence of the eastward front of the polecat's main range with the reintroduced population in the VCs of Herts, Bedford and Bucks partly explains the greater eastward extent of the range immediately to the north-west of London.

The Severn estuary, the Avon Gorge and Bristol City were probably temporary obstacles to the spread southward from Wales and the Marches into the South-west

45

Peninsula; now, polecats have successfully dispersed southward, skirting to the east of Bristol and into North Somerset, so expansion westward towards Devon is likely from here and also from the Dorset and Wiltshire populations. Consolidation of the polecat's range in central southern England means that, conditions permitting, the way is now clear for expansion eastward into the remaining 'blank' areas in East Anglia and to the south of London.

Polecat populations arising from reintroductions since the 1970s have achieved mixed success: those in southern England reported by Birks (1999a) have now become incorporated within the polecat's main range as it expanded, and some occupy areas of medium (e.g. Bedford and North Hants VCs) or even high purity (Bucks VC); the reintroduced population in North-west England persists but is of low purity and shows little sign of expansion; similarly, a reintroduced population of low purity appears to be established in Perthshire; no evidence was found of the reintroduced Argyll population; and a population of uncertain origin was confirmed in Sutherland and Caithness. One conclusion that could be drawn from this brief summary is that reintroduced populations that are effectively isolated from large populations of relatively high purity (such as those at the core of the polecat's main range), suffer greater introgression with ferrets and this may adversely affect both their purity and performance. This presupposes that the original donor stock comprised true polecats, something that is impossible to confirm because of the covert nature of most of the releases reported by Birks (1999a).

6.2 The significance of introgression with ferrets

The conservation implications of interactions between polecats and ferrets in Britain have been considered and clarified by Davison *et al.* (1998, 2000) and Kitchener *et al.* (1999). They suggested that, despite much evidence of reproductive introgression between wild polecats and escaped or feral ferrets (a process that must have occurred ever since the ferret became widely established as a working domestic animal in Britain by the fourteenth century; Kitchener & Birks, 2008), the polecat phenotype carries competitive advantages that enable it to assert itself widely over 'ferrety' forms within the polecat's main range in Britain. Kitchener *et al.* (1999) identified geographical trends in the proportion of animals with a 'ferrety' phenotype that were consistent with greater introgression toward the fringes of the polecat's main range and in reintroduced populations. This geographical analysis is developed further through the Polecat Purity Zones defined in the present survey. A similar zoned approach, based upon geographical variations in the proportion of 'pure' specimens, has been adopted in conservation planning for the Scottish wildcat *Felis silvestris*, the other wild British carnivore affected by introgression with a domestic or feral congener (Macdonald *et al.*, 2004).

One result that emerged unexpectedly from the present survey may amount to indirect evidence of competitive interaction between polecats and ferrets in the wild; importantly, it prompts us to suggest mechanisms through which the polecat phenotype asserts itself where polecats and ferrets are sympatric. The observation in Section 5.5.1 that, compared with polecats, polecat-ferrets were under-represented in the autumn sample of RTCs (coinciding with the annual peak in dispersing juveniles; Birks, 1999a) supports a hypothesis of differences in reproductive fitness and/or survival between the two forms in the wild in Britain. It suggests that while polecat-ferrets are apparently active participants during the spring polecat mating season, this leads to proportionately fewer dispersing juvenile polecat-ferrets in the following autumn compared with true polecats. This difference between the two forms might be explained in any or all of the following ways:

● Male polecat-ferrets compete poorly with true polecats for mates during the mating season, so proportionately fewer polecat-ferrets are fathered;

- Female polecat-ferrets suffer poor survival compared with true polecats when pregnant in the wild, so produce fewer viable litters;
- Female polecat-ferrets produce smaller litters than true polecats;
- Juvenile polecat-ferrets suffer poor survival in the wild compared with juvenile polecats;
- Juvenile polecat-ferrets are less active dispersers than juvenile polecats.

Further research will be needed to determine which, if any, of these scenarios is primarily responsible for the observed differences in abundance of polecats and polecat-ferrets in the autumn RTC figures. Nevertheless, this evidence of a significant difference between the two forms in Britain provides valuable support for the cautiously optimistic speculation by Kitchener *et al.* (1999) about the future genetic integrity of wild polecats. It also suggests that, on current evidence, there is no case for selective culling of feral ferrets or polecat-ferrets in the wild in Britain in order to maintain the integrity of the polecat population. This contrasts sharply with the situation facing the Scottish wildcat, in which hybridisation with domestic or feral cats is a major threat to wildcat conservation and a zoned approach is proposed to limit the flow of domestic cat genes into the wildcat population (Macdonald *et al.*, 2004).

6.3 The polecat's place in the carnivore guild

A question of both practical and academic interest concerns the nature of any interactions between a recovering polecat population and that of other wild carnivores in Britain; how do changes in the distribution and abundance of members of the carnivore guild impact upon each other and the resources they might compete for? In this respect the twentieth century was a dynamic period, especially among carnivores in southern Britain: it witnessed the expansion of the polecat population (Birks, 1999a); the dramatic fall and subsequent initial recovery of the Eurasian otter *Lutra lutra* population (Jefferies, 1989; Jefferies *et al.*, 2003); the establishment and spread of the American mink *Mustela vison* (Jefferies *et al.*, 2003); and increases in populations of both the red fox *Vulpes vulpes* (Tapper, 1992) and European badger *Meles meles* (Wilson *et al.*, 1997). Though such intra-guild relationships are notoriously difficult to study, some authors have sought to shed light on the polecat's place in the carnivore guild. Notably and most recently, a study by Harrington (2007) has investigated intra-guild interactions between the polecat, American mink and otter.

The American mink and European polecat are morphologically very similar, so it is unsurprising that there is evidence of competitive interaction between them. On the basis of widespread character displacement detected in the dentition of British and Irish mustelids, Dayan and Simberloff (1994) speculated that in Britain the invasive American mink was occupying the niche vacated by the polecat following its near-eradication by humans. In Eastern Europe, the arrival of the American mink led to reductions in the numbers of both European polecats and European mink *Mustela lutreola* in riparian habitats (Sidorovich & Macdonald, 2001) and changes in the sex ratios of these species, with females the losers in both cases (Sidorovich, 2000). While radio-tracking mink and polecats in the Thames Valley in Oxfordshire, Harrington and Macdonald (in press) detected evidence of temporal partitioning of activity (polecats nocturnal; mink diurnal) and incomplete habitat partitioning that might enable coexistence of the two species where home ranges overlapped.

In Britain the polecat currently shows less selection for riparian habitats than is typically the case in continental Europe (Birks, 1998; Birks & Kitchener, 1999c; Lodé, 1997; Rondinini *et al.*, 2006). The super-abundance of rabbits in Britain has been suggested as one explanation for this difference (Birks & Kitchener, 1999c); but perhaps intra-guild pressures following the invasion of riparian habitats by mink are also involved, forcing polecats to adopt more terrestrial habits than they would in the absence of mink? A further twist to the tale is provided by the current recovery of the otter in Britain: Harrington and Macdonald (in press) suggest that its dominant presence over mink in the riparian zone may push mink into greater contact with polecats in terrestrial habitats. There is much still to learn about the polecat's relations with other carnivores in Britain. However, it is encouraging to note that the widespread presence of mink and the current recovery of the otter have not apparently curtailed the polecat's continuing range expansion.

6.4 People and polecats

In the current era of ecological awareness and general sympathy towards wildlife in Britain, human attitudes towards the polecat are bound to be more favourable than those that prevailed in the past. The intensity of human loathing and lethal culling directed towards the polecat when it was last common and widespread in Britain is revealed in Roger Lovegrove's book *Silent Fields* (Lovegrove, 2007) based upon numbers killed of various species listed in old parish records. Classed as vermin and with a price on its head since Tudor times, the polecat was killed in more parishes in England and Wales between the seventeenth and nineteenth centuries than any other mammal apart from the fox; further, apart from the mole *Talpa europea,* no other animal was killed in such huge numbers as the polecat.

One likely explanation for the great scale of this historical interaction lies in the polecat's long-standing affinity with human habitations and farmsteads. No doubt attracted by prey (such as poultry and commensal rodents) and sheltered resting sites, for centuries polecats in Britain have chosen to live closer to humans than any other wild carnivore. Blandford (1987) describes examples of this behaviour from several countries, including a 14th century mention in Chaucer's *The Pardoner's Tale* of "a polecat too about my yard that takes my chickens". There is a paradox in our early relations with the polecat: though its close affinity with human dwellings fuelled hatred and persecution of the species among our forbears, it may also have been the key factor in the process of domestication in southern Europe that produced the ferret some 2000 years ago. Today, as then, the common occurrence of orphaned polecat kits close to houses provides opportunities for humans to rear them in captivity.

Clearly, the association between wild polecats and human dwellings revealed by the present survey is entirely consistent with the species' normal behaviour over many centuries, and should not be viewed as atypical or 'ferrety' behaviour. However, most visits by polecats to gardens probably go unnoticed because of their rapid, furtive and nocturnal nature (e.g. Clark, 2006). Since there is evidence that brown rat *Rattus norvegicus* populations outside houses are increasing, possibly due to climate change to which rats are responding favourably (CSL, 2005), and to other activities such as the increase in home composting (Rowlatt, 2007), we might expect more visits to our gardens from foraging polecats in future. This will be a cause of pleasure to many people and concern to some, according to the findings of the present survey.

People and polecats in Britain interact in many other ways that will shape our perceptions of the species, and could influence its future in Britain: fluctuations in the intensity of predator control have seen the polecat very nearly eliminated from Britain and, currently, returning to its former haunts; latterly we gave the polecat some legal protection and priority listing as a UK BAP species; we have created rural landscapes in which polecats thrive (McDonald & Birks, 2003), though human-induced climate change and land management responses to it offer an uncertain future; we introduced two important prey species that currently flourish as agricultural pests, the brown rat and the rabbit; yet the methods we use to control these pests may inadvertently harm or kill polecats, notably fumigation of rabbit burrows (Birks & Kitchener, 1999c) and the use of rodenticides (Birks, 1998; Shore *et al.*, 2003); we have allowed a domesticated congener, the ferret, to escape and breed with wild polecats, leading to phenotypic variation and associated identification uncertainties among biological recorders and others; consequently most people, even in the polecat's Welsh heartland, do not recognise the animal when shown photographs of it (Birks, 1993; Williamson & Birks, 2005); where our husbandry systems fail, polecats predate our domestic stock and penned game, and suffer injury or death in spring traps used for predator control (Packer & Birks, 1999); and finally, attracted to forage along road corridors populated by live prey and strewn with fresh carrion, many polecats die each year as road traffic casualties. A brief appraisal of this list confirms that conservation action is justified on several fronts, both to benefit polecats and the people with any interest in them.

7. RECOMMENDATIONS FOR CONSERVATION ACTION

The polecat is now a UK Biodiversity Action Plan priority species. Although no national Species Action Plan is in place or proposed, the broad action categories identified during the UK BAP Species and Habitats Review comprised habitat based wider action, surveys to monitor changes in distribution, and research into taxonomy and genetics in connection with introgression with ferrets (UK BAP, 2007). Despite the improving trend in the polecat's conservation status confirmed during the present survey, there are further areas where conservation action is justified at a national or local level. A traditional antipathy towards predators in some communities means that rehabilitation of recovering carnivores presents cultural as well as physical challenges (Birks, 2000; Yalden, 1993). Action is required simply to address the lack of knowledge and understanding of this native mustelid as it reoccupies the countryside around us; other actions are more specific and technical, such as those required to limit the ill-effects upon polecat populations of rodenticide use. The sections below reiterate and expand upon those suggested by Birks (1999b) in the previous VWT survey report by Birks & Kitchener (1999a).

7.1 Key aims

The following key aims are suggested as the basis for conservation action on wild polecats in Britain:

- To maintain polecats at favourable conservation status wherever populations occur in Britain
- To promote continued expansion of the polecat's main range in southern Britain
- To establish expanding populations of true polecats in northern Britain

7.2 Key actions

The following sections identify actions proposed as a means to achieving the key aims suggested in 7.1 above:

7.2.1 Maintaining and enhancing habitat quality

The polecat is not a habitat specialist. However, evidence from continental Europe suggests that general degradation of habitats, and drainage of wetlands in particular, have affected polecat populations adversely (Birks & Kitchener, 1999b). Certain features of the farmed landscape are clearly important to polecats, such as hedgerows and woodland edges (Birks, 1998). On intensive farmland in Britain the loss of such features and the limited extent of semi-natural habitat and poor prey availability could be a serious constraint for the species.

- Research should be carried out on variations in the performance of polecat populations in different landscapes, through field studies and population modelling. The likely effects of climate change on polecat habitats and prey populations should be identified.
- The results of such research should be used to guide the development of policies to improve degraded agricultural landscapes in ways that benefit polecats and their prey.

7.2.2 Reducing the secondary effects of rodenticides

Polecats are vulnerable to secondary poisoning through predation upon rodents contaminated with anticoagulant rodenticides (Birks, 1998; Shore *et al.*, 2003). Up

50

to 50% of the polecat population may be exposed to such poisons each winter and an unknown proportion dies as a result. There are concerns about the effect upon polecat recovery of the greater use of rodenticides in the east of England, at and beyond the current limits of the species' range.

- Regular, structured monitoring of background rodenticide exposure levels should be undertaken by screening the livers of polecats that have lived through the main mid-winter period of rodenticide use.

- An assessment of the population effects of rodenticide poisoning in polecats should be undertaken. This should include research to identify the lethal doses, sub-lethal effects and metabolism characteristics in polecats of widely-used rodenticides.

- Prior to approval, new rodenticide products should be subject to a thorough assessment of the toxicological risk they pose to polecats and other predatory species.

- High standards should be established and maintained in the proper use of rodenticides, with a view to minimising non-target effects such as secondary poisoning.

7.2.3 Reducing mortality in spring traps

The legality of unlicensed trapping requires clarification. Polecats are commonly caught in lethal spring traps set in tunnels (commonly known as 'tunnel traps'; Packer & Birks, 1999); some spring traps are ineffective at killing polecats humanely (Section 5.5.3, present study). Many trappers believe that this form of 'accidental' culling is acceptable, despite a legal requirement to take reasonable steps to avoid it. The polecat is spreading into areas of heavier trapping pressure in eastern England (Birks, 2000) where there is a greater likelihood of adverse but avoidable effects upon populations.

- Where possible, the use of spring traps should be avoided on land where polecats might be present; where spring traps are used within or near the polecat's distributional range, custom-built exclusion devices on tunnel entrances (Short & Reynolds, 2001) should be actively promoted as a requirement to avoid accidental injury to non-target species such as polecats.

- Relevant conservation and welfare organisations, licensing authorities and bodies representing game shooting interests should seek to agree and promote a code of conduct regarding the accidental capture of polecats in cage and spring traps. This should state clearly the legal position regarding the use of exclusion devices and the accidental killing of polecats.

7.2.4 Reducing road traffic casualties

The polecat is very vulnerable to road traffic; RTCs are the commonest form of recorded mortality in Britain. Where traffic densities are high, RTC mortality may lead to adverse population effects such as population sinks and barriers to dispersal.

- Research should be carried out to identify the effects of road traffic upon polecat populations in Britain.

- Mitigation measures to reduce polecat RTC mortality and facilitate dispersal through areas of high traffic density by expanding populations should be identified and incorporated in the Design Manual for Roads and Bridges (Highways Agency, 2008).

7.2.5 Reducing introgression with feral ferrets

All wild polecat populations are affected to some extent by introgression (interbreeding) with ferrets, though the polecat phenotype appears dominant in the long term. Evidence of introgression is greatest towards the fringes of the polecat's expanding range and in isolated populations established through reintroductions (Section 5.4.7).

● Patterns of introgression should be monitored at ten-year intervals through structured sampling of polecats, feral ferrets and introgressive hybrids throughout mainland Britain. Morphometric assessment of specimens should be used to update the Polecat Purity Zones identified in the present survey.

● Microsatellite DNA fingerprinting techniques should be applied to improve understanding of patterns of genetic variation in polecats and ferrets; this should include assessments of the genetic status of isolated polecat populations, such as the one in Caithness and East Sutherland; it should also seek to resolve and update the taxonomy of polecats and ferrets.

● Measures to reduce the numbers of fertile ferrets lost or escaping into the wild should be promoted in partnership with ferret-keeping and ferret welfare organisations.

7.2.6 Improving confidence and rigour in polecat recording

A widespread lack of familiarity with the distinction between true polecats and polecat-ferrets is a significant hindrance to effective recording in Britain.

● A simple guide should be produced to illustrate the key external differences between true polecats, polecat-ferrets and other colour morphs (building on Kitchener, 2002); this should enable BRCs to build confidence in verifying records.

● Recorders should be encouraged to provide photographic evidence of specimens to enable verification by BRCs.

7.2.7 Promoting tolerance and understanding

Polecats commonly visit gardens, farmsteads, houses and outbuildings to forage, rest and sometimes to breed; while most visits go unnoticed, some may lead to problems, both real and imagined. For example, polecats may predate penned game and poultry if husbandry systems fail. This may lead to needless intolerance and demands for removal or 'control' of polecats. There is a strong case for promoting greater awareness of the polecat as a recovering native mammal of high conservation value.

● A general information leaflet on polecats (building on the series produced by the VWT) should be produced and distributed, especially toward the fringes of the polecat's expanding range where people are likely to be least familiar with the species.

● Sustainable husbandry solutions, in the form of sound housing and pens for game and poultry, to the possibility of polecat predation should be promoted as an alternative to lethal control.

7.2.8 Distribution-mapping

The polecat's distribution in Britain is likely to continue changing in the future until the current phase of range expansion ceases. Active distribution-mapping is essential as a means to plot and understand such changes.

● Polecat distribution-mapping should be carried out at ten-year intervals in Britain. Such surveys should be based mainly on the collection of evidence suitable for assessing phenotype of specimens (carcasses or photographs).

● Because of the time that has elapsed since some 10km squares, particularly in Wales, were last confirmed as positive for polecat presence since 1950, such squares should be targeted for recording in the next survey.

7.2.9 Confirming the status of outlier populations

Beyond the polecat's main range in Wales and central England lie isolated populations of low purity or uncertain status, most of which are believed to result from reintroductions since 1970.

- The status of the polecat population in Caithness and East Sutherland should be the subject of a special study to confirm its status as a product of either a reintroduction or long term survival.

- Recording effort should be directed towards confirming the persistence or otherwise of polecat populations in Argyll and beside Loch Ness reported by earlier authors (e.g. Craik & Brown, 1997; Jones, 1992) but not confirmed as extant during the present survey.

- Further survey work should be undertaken to establish the true extent of the reintroduced population in North-west England, and to establish the reasons for its limited recent range expansion.

- A strategy should be developed to facilitate the wide scale re-establishment of true polecats in northern Britain.

7.2.10 Monitoring abundance

Distribution-mapping cannot be expected to provide information on changes in the abundance of polecats within their main range. Such changes are important indicators of conservation successes or problems. It is important to study these changes by monitoring patterns of polecat abundance in Britain.

- The VWT's annual polecat and mink abundance monitoring system, based upon hand-picked recorders noting RTCs seen against mileage driven during September and October, should be validated and modified, if necessary, to provide robust data on changes in polecat abundance in time and space.

8. REFERENCES

ANON. (2005). Pick up a polecat! Mammal News 143: p.5.

ARNOLD, H.R. (1978). Provisional atlas of the mammals of the British Isles. Institute of Terrestrial Ecology, Abbots Ripton, UK.

ARNOLD, H.R. (1984). Distribution Maps of the Mammals of the British Isles. Institute of Terrestrial Ecology, Abbots Ripton, UK.

ARNOLD, H.R. (1993). Atlas of Mammals in Britain. Institute of Terrestrial Ecology, Abbots Ripton, UK.

BIRKS, J. (1993). The return of the polecat. British Wildlife, 5, (1) pp.16-25.

BIRKS, J.D.S. (1998). Secondary rodenticide poisoning risk arising from winter farmyard use by the European Polecat *Mustela putorius*. Biological Conservation 85, 233-240.

BIRKS, J.D.S. (1999a). A survey of polecat distribution in Britain, 1993-1997. pp. 28-54 in The distribution and status of the polecat *Mustela putorius* in Britain in the 1990s. eds. J.D.S. Birks & A.C. Kitchener. The Vincent Wildlife Trust. London.

BIRKS, J.D.S. (1999b). Recommendations for polecat conservation in Britain. pp. 131-134 in The distribution and status of the polecat *Mustela putorius* in Britain in the 1990s. eds. J.D.S. Birks & A.C. Kitchener. The Vincent Wildlife Trust. London.

BIRKS, J.D.S. (2000). The recovery of the polecat (*Mustela putorius*) in Britain. Pp. 141-152 in Griffiths H.I. (ed.) Mustelids in a modern world: Management and conservation aspects of small carnivore: human interactions. Backhuys. Leiden.

BIRKS, J. (2004). The silent return of the polecat. Natural World 72: p.29.

BIRKS, J. (2006). Have you seen this animal? BBC Wildlife 24 (3): 36-41.

BIRKS, J.D.S., HANSON P., JERMYN D.L., SCHOFIELD H.W. & WALTON K.C. (1999). Development of a method for monitoring polecats. pp. 55-83 in The distribution and status of the polecat *Mustela putorius* in Britain in the 1990s. eds. J.D.S. Birks & A.C. Kitchener. The Vincent Wildlife Trust. London.

BIRKS, J.D.S. & KITCHENER A.C., EDS. (1999a). The distribution and status of the polecat *Mustela putorius* in Britain in the 1990s. The Vincent Wildlife Trust. London.

BIRKS, J.D.S. & KITCHENER A.C. (1999b). The background to the VWT Polecat Survey. pp. 13-27 in The distribution and status of the polecat *Mustela putorius* in Britain in the 1990s. eds. J.D.S. Birks & A.C. Kitchener. The Vincent Wildlife Trust. London.

BIRKS, J.D.S. & KITCHENER A.C. (1999c). Ecology of the polecat in lowland England. pp. 111-130 in The distribution and status of the polecat *Mustela putorius* in Britain in the 1990s. eds. J.D.S. Birks & A.C. Kitchener. The Vincent Wildlife Trust. London.

BIRKS, J.D.S. & KITCHENER, A.C. (2008). Polecat. pp. 476-485 In Mammals of the British Isles Handbook 4th edition. eds. Harris, S. & Yalden, D.W. The Mammal Society, Southampton.

BLANDFORD, P.R.S. (1987). Biology of the Polecat *Mustela putorius*: a literature review. Mammal Review 17 (4) 155-198.

BUCKLEY, D.J. & SLEEMAN, D.P. (2007). Feral ferrets *Mustela putorius furo* L. in Ireland. Irish Naturalists' Journal 28 (9) 356-360.

CLARK, M. (2006). Polecats as regular garden visitors. Transactions of the Hertfordshire Natural History Society, 38 (2) 175-176.

CORBET, G.H. (1971). Provisional distribution maps of British mammals. Mammal Review 1 (4/5) 95-142.

CRAIK, J.C.A. & BROWN, D. (1997). Polecats in the West of Scotland. Glasgow Naturalist 23 (2) 50-53.

CSL. (2005). Rodent infestations in domestic properties in England, 2001. DEFRA, London.

DAVISON, A., BIRKS, J.D.S., GRIFFITHS, H.I., KITCHENER, A.C., BIGGINS, D. & BUTLIN, R.K. (1998). Hybridization and the phylogenetic relationship between polecats and domestic ferrets in Britain. Biological Conservation. 87 (2), 155-162.

DAVISON, A., BIRKS, J.D.S., MARAN, T., MACDONALD, D.W., SIDOROVICH, V., GRIFFITHS, H.I. & BUTLIN, R.K. (2000). Conservation implications of hybridization between polecats, ferrets and European mink (*Mustela* sp.). pp. 153-162 in Griffiths H.I. (ed.) Mustelids in a modern world: Management and conservation aspects of small carnivore: human interactions. Backhuys. Leiden.

DAYAN, T. & SIMBERLOFF, D. (1994). Character displacement, sexual dimorphism, and morphological variation among British and Irish mustelids. Ecology 75: 1063-1073.

HARRINGTON, L.A. (2007). The American mink, *Mustela vison*: its management and interactions with two native mustelids, the European polecat, *M. putorius*, and the Eurasian otter, *Lutra lutra.* Unpubl. Ph.D. thesis, University of Oxford.

HARRINGTON, L.A. & MACDONALD, D.W. (in press). Spatial and temporal relationships between two similar mustelids in southern UK: the invasive American mink and the native European polecat. Journal of Mammalogy.

HIGHWAYS AGENCY (2008). http://www.standardsforhighways.co.uk/dmrb/index.htm

JEFFERIES, D.J. (1989). The changing otter population of Britain 1700-1989. Biological Journal of the Linnean Society, 38: 61-69.

JEFFERIES, D.J., STRACHAN, C. & STRACHAN, R. (2003). Estimated numbers of the three interacting riparian mammals in Britain using survey data. pp. 188-199 in The water vole and mink survey of Britain 1996-1998 with a history of the long term changes in the status of both species and their causes. Jefferies, D.J. (ed.). The Vincent Wildlife Trust, Ledbury, UK.

JONES, P. (1992). An assessment of the feasibility of re-introducing the polecat (*Mustela putorius*) in to populated rural areas of England, with special reference to Dartmoor. Unpublished BSc. Honours project. Seal-Hayne College.

KITCHENER, A. (2002). Polecats and Ferrets: how to tell them apart. The Vincent Wildlife Trust, Ledbury.

KITCHENER, A.C. & BIRKS, J.D.S. (2008). Feral Ferret. pp. 485-487 In Mammals of the British Isles Handbook 4th edition. eds. Harris, S. & Yalden, D.W. The Mammal Society, Southampton.

KITCHENER, A.C., BIRKS, J.D.S. & DAVISON, A. (1999). Interactions between polecats and ferrets in Britain. Pp. 84-110 in The distribution and status of the polecat *Mustela putorius* in Britain in the 1990s. eds. J.D.S. Birks & A.C. Kitchener. The Vincent Wildlife Trust. London.

LANGLEY, P.J.W. & YALDEN, D.W. (1977). The decline of the rarer carnivores in Great Britain during the nineteenth century. Mammal Review 7 (3/4) 95-116.

LODÉ, T. (1997). Trophic status and feeding habits of the European Polecat *Mustela putorius* L. 1758. Mammal Review, 27 (4) 177-184.

LOVEGROVE, R. (2007). Silent Fields: the long decline of a nation's wildlife. Oxford University Press, Oxford.

McDONALD, R.A. & BIRKS, J.D.S. (2003). Effects of farming practice and wildlife management on small mustelid carnivores. Pages 106-119 in Tattersall, F. & W. Manley, (eds.) Conservation & Conflict: Mammals and Farming in Britain. Linnean Society Occasional Publication 4.

MACDONALD, D.W., DANIELS, M.J., DRISCOLL, C., KITCHENER, A.C. & YAMAGUCHI, N. (2004). The Scottish wildcat: Analyses for conservation and an Action Plan. Wildlife Conservation Research Group, Oxford.

PACKER, J.J. & BIRKS, J.D.S. (1999). An assessment of British farmers' and gamekeepers' experiences, attitudes and practices in relation to the European Polecat *Mustela putorius.* Mammal Review 29: 75-92.

PERTOLDI, C., BREYNE, P., CABRIA, M. T., HALFMAERTEN, D., JANSMAN, H. A. H., VAN DEN BERGE, K., MADSEN, A.B. & LOESCHCKE, V. (2006). Genetic structure of the European polecat (*Mustela putorius*) and its implication for conservation strategies. 270: 102-115.

RONDININI, C., ERCOLI, V. & BOITANI, L. (2006). Habitat use and preference by polecats (*Mustela putorius* L.) in a Mediterranean agricultural landscape. Journal of Zoology 269: 213-219.

ROWLATT, J. (2007). http://www.bbc.co.uk/blogs/newsnight/2007/01/theres_a_rat_ in_me_compost.html

SHORE, R.F., BIRKS, J.D.S., AFSAR, A., WIENBURG, C.L. & KITCHENER, A.C. (2003). Spatial and temporal analysis of second-generation anticoagulant rodenticide residues in polecats (*Mustela putorius*) from throughout their range in Britain, 1992-1999. Environmental Pollution 122:183-193.

SHORT, M.J. & REYNOLDS, J.C. (2001). Physical exclusion of non-target species in tunnel-trapping of mammalian pests. Biological Conservation 98: 139-147.

SIDOROVICH, V.E. (2000). The on-going decline of riparian mustelids (European mink, *Mustela lutreola,* polecat, *Mustela putorius,* and stoat, *Mustela erminea*) in eastern Europe: a review of the results to date. pp. 295-319 in: Mustelids in a modern world. Griffiths, H.I (ed.). Backhuys, Leiden, The Netherlands.

SIDOROVICH, V.E. & MACDONALD, D.W. (2001). Density dynamics and changes in habitat use by the European mink and other native mustelids in connection with the American mink expansion in Belarus. Netherlands Journal of Zoology, 51: 107-126.

SOLOW, A.R., KITCHENER, A.C., ROBERTS, D.L. & BIRKS, J.D.S. (2006). Rediscovery of the Scottish polecat, *Mustela putorius*: Survival or reintroduction? Biological Conservation 128: 574-575.

TAPPER, S. (1992). Game Heritage. Game Conservancy Ltd., Fordingbridge.

TEALL, N. (1982). A Natural Survivor? The polecat in Britain. Country Life, December 9th 1982.

UK BAP. (2007). http://www.ukbap.org.uk/newprioritylist.aspx

WALTON, K.C. (1964). The distribution of the polecat (*Putorius putorius*) in England, Wales and Scotland, 1959-62. Proceedings of the Zoological Society of London, 143, 333-336.

WALTON, K.C. (1968). The distribution of the polecat, *Putorius putorius*, in Great Britain, 1963-67. Journal of Zoology, London, 155 (2), 237-240.

WILLIAMSON. K. & BIRKS, J. (2005). Time to fly the flag for the polecat. Natur Cymru 17: 18-22.

WILSON, G., HARRIS, S. & McLAREN, G. (1997). Changes in the British badger population, 1988 to 1997. People's Trust for Endangered Species, London.

YALDEN, D.W. (1993). The problems of reintroducing carnivores. Symposia of the Zoological Society of London, 65: 289-306.

9. APPENDICES

Appendix 1 A5 flyer inviting people to participate in the survey.

Pick up a Polecat!
Help with The Mammal Society and VWT Polecat Distribution Survey 2004-2006

The Mammal Society and The Vincent Wildlife Trust (VWT) are using road casualties to record the current distribution of the polecat in Britain and also to carry out studies on the bodies sent in. If you would like to help with this survey, it is wise to carry a camera, plastic bags (min. 40x30cm), disposable gloves and antiseptic wipes in your vehicle.

What to do if you see a dead polecat on the road:

- Park safely and watch out for other road traffic
- The casualty is almost certainly dead but check for signs of life before touching the animal (if alive, do not touch it)
- If the animal is badly squashed, or you are not able to collect it, please take photos (showing complete back view, underside and head if possible)
- Use plastic bags or gloves to recover the body, taking care to avoid contact with body fluids and parasites such as ticks
- Securely seal the body in plastic bags and keep it cool (ideally deep-frozen)
- Phone the VWT on 01531 636441 for instructions (you may be asked to post the body in packaging supplied by the VWT)
- Record the date you found the polecat, the six figure grid reference and nearest town/village. Keep these details with the body along with your name
- Please remember also to send these details to your County Mammal Recorder (contact details available from The Mammal Society).

Make sure you do not compromise your safety nor that of other road users.

By taking part in the Polecat Distribution Survey you will be helping us to determine the distribution of this elusive carnivore and allow us to monitor future changes.

Polecat-ferrets are usually paler than polecats.

Following the polecat's near-extinction in Britain in the early 1900s, a 1993-1997 VWT polecat survey confirmed the partial recovery of the population and an expansion of its range from Wales into the English Midlands. It also confirmed the existence of introduced populations elsewhere in England and in parts of Scotland.

The new 2004-2006 Polecat Distribution Survey is run by The Mammal Society and The Vincent Wildlife Trust. We aim to produce a new distribution map for the polecat in Britain and to identify the presence of any feral ferret populations on the mainland. We are working with the National Museums of Scotland and the Centre for Ecology and Hydrology to carry out a range of studies on the specimens collected.

Photos: Johnny Birks/VWT

- We can accept records without accompanying photos or body, though these are less valuable because we cannot confirm their identity as true polecats or hybrids.

- We are also interested in feral ferrets and polecat-ferret hybrids as well as polecats so please pick these up too.

- Occasionally we won't need any more dead bodies from your area so please don't be offended if we don't need the one you have found!

- There is no need to pre-register to take part in the survey.

For more information on the polecat survey please contact the VWT or visit its website.

Appendix 2   Guidelines sent out to contributors to the survey who contacted the VWT about a specimen they had recovered.

THE VWT/MAMMAL SOCIETY POLECAT SURVEY 2004-2006

GUIDELINES FOR POSTING SPECIMENS TO THE VWT

Thank you for contacting the VWT about a polecat or polecat-ferret specimen that you have found. We have consulted the Royal Mail about this survey and have established that it is acceptable to post bodies of dead animals so long as they are properly packaged. The packaging supplied with this sheet meets this requirement. Now please follow these steps:

1. Remove all items from the cardboard box. There should be a specimen form, two seal-able plastic bags, a stamped, addressed envelope, an address label, leaflets about polecats and the current survey, disposable gloves and this sheet.

2. Clearly write all the details requested on the specimen form, including your name and contact details (otherwise we cannot send you feedback on the progress of the survey).

3. Write your name with a ballpoint or permanent marker pen on one of the white panels on one of the two seal-able plastic bags supplied in the box.

4. Place the specimen (ideally deep-frozen, but this is not essential) inside the named plastic bag and seal it, taking care to exclude as much air as possible. Please check that the bag is properly sealed.

5. Place the specimen form and the named bag containing the specimen into the second seal-able bag; then seal the bag after excluding the air as before. The specimen should now be contained within two sealed bags with the completed specimen form separated from the specimen in the outer bag.

6. Place the bagged specimen in the cardboard box supplied; wrap and pad it well with light, recyclable insulating material (such as newspaper) so that the specimen does not move about inside the box.

7. Close the box, put on the return address sticker and use parcel tape to secure the front flap so that it cannot come open.

8. Take both box and S.A.E. to a Post Office and, if total box weight is not over 2kg, ask for the box to be sent 'guaranteed next day delivery' (this should cost £7.40). If the weight exceeds 2kg (next day delivery would cost £18.50!) please send it by standard parcel delivery (2-4kg parcels currently cost £7.70). Ask for a receipt, write your name on the back and place it in the S.A.E. provided and post it to us so that we can reimburse you. Please try to post specimens early in the week so as to avoid the risk of a Saturday delivery when our office is closed.

9. Finally, it would be very helpful if you could 'phone 01531 636441 to let us know when you have posted the specimen. Thank You!

The Vincent Wildlife Trust, 3&4 Bronsil Courtyard, Eastnor, Ledbury, HR8 1EP.
01531 636441 • vwt@vwt.org.uk

Appendix 3 The number of verifiable records of true polecats and polecat-ferrets from 2004-2006, broken down by vice-county. Those vice-counties with fewer than five verifiable records are highlighted in dark green, because such small samples undermine the value of the % True Polecats figure.

Vice-County	True polecats	Polecat-ferrets	% True polecats	No. 'dark polecat-ferrets'	No. 'pale polecat-ferrets'
Anglesey	3	1	75.0		1
Bedford	17	2	89.5	1	1
Berks	25	2	92.6		2
Brecon	27		100.0		
Bucks	11		100.0		
Caernarvon	25	2	92.6	1	1
Caithness	4	1	80.0	1	
Cambridge		1	0.0		1
Cardigan	25		100.0		
Carmarthen	9		100.0		
Chester	42	2	95.5	2	
Cheviotland	1	2	33.3		2
Cumberland	11	6	64.7	3	3
Denbigh	13	3	81.3	1	2
Derby	27	8	77.1	6	2
Dorset	14	8	63.6	5	3
Durham		3	0.0	1	2
East Cornwall		1	0.0	1	
East Gloucester	15	1	93.8		1
East Norfolk		1	0.0	1	
East Perth	3	2	60.0	2	
East Ross		2	0.0		2
East Suffolk		1	0.0		1
East Sussex		1	0.0		1
East Sutherland	1	1	50.0		1
Fife		1	0.0	1	
Flint	9		100.0		
Glamorgan	31	3	91.2	3	
Hereford	58	2	96.7	1	1
Herts	9	4	69.2	4	
Hunts	1		100.0		
Kincardine		1	0.0		1
Kirkcudbright		1	0.0	1	
Lanark	1		100.0		
Leicester	3	2	60.0	2	
Merioneth	30	1	96.8	1	
Mid Perth		4	0.0		4
Mid-West York	1	3	25.0	2	1
Monmouth	22	1	95.7	1	
Montgomery	15		100.0		
North Devon		1	0.0		1

Vice-County	True polecats	Polecat-ferrets	% True polecats	No. 'dark polecat-ferrets'	No. 'pale polecat-ferrets'
North Essex	1	3	25.0	2	1
North Hants	25	3	89.3	2	1
North Lincoln	1	3	25.0		3
North Somerset	3		100.0		
North Wilts	18	3	85.7	2	1
Northampton	16		100.0		
North-East York		2	0.0	1	1
Notts	1	2	33.3		2
Oxford	34	1	97.1		1
Pembroke	6		100.0		
Radnor	7		100.0		
Salop	43		100.0		
South Devon		4	0.0	3	1
South Essex		1	0.0		1
South Hants	14	6	70.0	5	1
South Somerset		1	0.0		1
South Wilts	6	1	85.7		1
Stafford	32	4	88.9	2	2
Surrey	5	3	62.5	2	1
Warwick	17	1	94.4		1
West Gloucester	20	3	87.0	2	1
West Lancaster	8	2	80.0	1	1
West Suffolk	1		100.0		
West Sussex	4	3	57.1		3
Westmorland	24	7	77.4	7	
Worcester	63		100.0		
Total	**802**	**128**	**86.2**	**70**	**58**

Appendix 4 Reports of polecats and polecat-ferrets seen in gardens and/or houses during 2004-2006.

Brief details of sighting	Location	Vice-county	Date
Seen in parents' garden	Wantage	22	10-Aug-04
Good close photos of a pure (pelage) polecat frolicking about in a garden in daylight. Behaviour suggests captive origin?	Prestbury	33	29-Sep-04
Obvious ferret photographed in garden at night.	Swaby	54	03-Nov-04
Photographed in garden	Walton-on-the-hill	39	06-Mar-05
Juvenile found in garden. Not well?	St Briavels	34	15-Jun-05
4 young polecats running in and out of house. Connected with possible breeding in outhouse.	Pen-y-bryn	41	15-Jun-05
Animal foraging in garden - appeared wild, breeding female?	Patchway	34	22-Jun-05
Two animals seen in garden in the evening, one eating frog.	Hale	58	01-Jul-05
4 baby polecats emerged from garden hedge at dusk. No sign of mother. I told him about orphan possibility and RSPCA rehab. project.	Maer	39	10-Jul-05
Three polecats spent day under chicken shed.	West Marden	13	17-Jul-05
Animal cornered in old duck house.	Llanover	35	19-Jul-05
Family party seen in garden a few times. Young one cornered and examined closely - good description. Concern about damage to garden and threat to children.	Wellington	40	22-Jul-05
Animal spotted at dusk in garden. Ran across patio and looked in through patio door.	Cheddleton	39	06-Aug-05
Seen in grounds of Snowdonia National Park Offices at 2pm	Penrhyndeudraeth	49	15-Aug-05
Polecat visits garden in evening to eat food put out for hedgehogs. Returned in 2006 and had 2 young in garden.	Llandrindod Wells	43	29-Aug-05
Animal found sleeping in a bag of grass clippings in a garden.	Overstrand	27	03-Sep-05
Seen in suburban garden late morning.	Tywyn	50	05-Sep-05
Animal seen playing in garden early morning. Living under shed?	Sandiacre	57	07-Sep-05
Animal cornered by Jack Russell in garden at 21:05h. Screeched. Observer sure it was polecat.	Leigh	9	12-Sep-05
Tame but pure-looking polecat feeding from dish of cat food in garden.	Wootton Bassett	7	15-Oct-05
Animal seen in garden at 3am. Took to living under conservatory and took food put out for foxes. Two polecats seen Aug 2006 after dark and videoed. Fed on chicken put out.	Walton-on-the-Hill	39	15-Oct-05
Animal seen in garden in daylight. Described as pure polecat by trained lab technician.	Cowbridge	41	26-Nov-05
Photographed in garden	Telford	40	10-Dec-05

Brief details of sighting	Location	Vice-county	Date
Found in chicken run, released.	Riddings	57	15-Dec-05
Polecat visits at Xmas time and breaks into kitchen through cat flap to eat cat food.	Llanfair Clydogau	44	25-Dec-05
Seen at night visiting to take fish heads.	Tewin Wood	20	07-Jan-06
Animal seen living in garden shed. Description sounds like a true polecat.	Rawnsley	39	15-Jan-06
Polecat-ferret visiting garden to eat food put out for fox	Farnham	17	14-Feb-06
Polecat chased young rabbit into garden, killed it then ran out into fields with it.	Minety	7	06-Jun-06
In garden at 3pm. Mother seen carrying 4 kits one by one to new den, then next day killed rabbit and dragged it across garden. Stood up to cat and spat at it to defend rabbit. Family stayed around for c. 1 month	Brown Moss	40	07-Jun-06
Juvenile polecat (named Henry) found crying on neighbours' lawn in village. Reared successfully and grew up tame, but living semi-free. Several photos supplied - pure polecat pelage.	Neston	7	10-Jun-06
Two polecats seen playing in garden at 08:10 hrs.	Menith Wood	37	10-Jul-06
Polecat playing on drive in morning	Glyn	35	11-Jul-06
Polecat seen in garden in morning	Princes Gate	45	11-Jul-06
Polecat appeared in garden, seemed timid & wild	Clovenfords	79	13-Jul-06
Family of dark polecats living under neighbour's garden shed. Seem wild.	Macclesfield	58	13-Jul-06
Seen twice in garden in daylight. Juv. polecat. First sighting it had just killed young blackbird and was being mobbed by adults.	Llansantffraid	47	15-Jul-06
Polecat family living under decking in garden. Fed and allowed to disperse.	Kidderminster	37	15-Jul-06
Family living under decking in garden. Fed and allowed to disperse.	Hartlebury	37	15-Jul-06
Polecat seen on lawn in garden in mid-afternoon	Llanfiar Caereinion	47	15-Jul-06
Family of mother and 2 young living under decking in garden. All trapped and taken into veterinary care by local Ferret Rescue, but mother released.	Kidderminster	37	17-Jul-06
Family of three seen in garden at 6am.	Wilmslow	58	18-Jul-06
Animal disturbed at 04:30h running around in rabbit enclosure trying to get into hutches. Observer and it had a 30 second staring match before it left.	Wistaston	58	19-Jul-06
Polecat seen in garden with dead rabbit	Selkirk	79	27-Jul-06
Family of 4 polecats or ferrets living under decking in garden. Very shy, but one tempted partly out to eat some minced beef. Moved on after a few days.	Macclesfield	58	28-Jul-06

Brief details of sighting	Location	Vice-county	Date
Polecat family under decking in urban garden. Husband dead against having them there, but wife more tolerant. Pest officer called in who trapped and removed four young and reared with his ferrets.	Caerphilly	41	30-Jul-06
Animal seen in garden at 5am for 20 mins., drinking from water bowls and generally foraging around bird feeding station. Cat took refuge on shed roof. Video sent to VWT.	Wilmslow	58	31-Jul-06
Family of 3+ polecats living in garage, fed on ferret food by owners.	Madeley	40	03-Aug-06
Family of polecats reported as living in garden shed and emerging to feed on frogs in neighbours' pond. Observer worried about damage so JB reassured her and sent leaflets.	Killay	41	08-Aug-06
'Polecat' broke in twice to brother's kitchen and took up residence under units. Desperate for advice to get it out without killing it.	Shrewsbury	40	14-Aug-06
Animal photographed in garden in morning. Very dark, but frontal brown band does not reach rhinarium.	Buntingford	20	15-Aug-06
Polecat visiting garden in evening.	Bridgnorth	40	21-Aug-06
Polecat seen in garden and fields behind house.	Bridgnorth	40	31-Aug-06
Seemed tame - visited garden in middle of town.	Crediton	3	31-Aug-06
Polecat living under garage in rabbit burrows.	Bredon	37	11-Sep-06
Family of adult + 2 juvs. filmed on edge of garden by old railway line.	Blunham	30	20-Sep-06
Polecat seen in garden at 08.30h. They will try to get photo	Middlewich	58	24-Sep-06
Polecat in garage. RSPCA came and failed to catch it. Confirmed as true polecat.	Hazel Grove	58	25-Sep-06
Animal living under garden shed	Marbury	58	28-Sep-06
No details.	Macclesfield	58	30-Sep-06
Animal seen to emerge from decking behind house.	Macclesfield	58	02-Oct-06
Polecat seen snuffling around shrubs at 10.30am	Middlewich	58	11-Oct-06
Polecat came to take cat's food outside house.	Longhope	34	12-Oct-06
Animal with very slight ferrety features visiting house and entering via catflap and in outside toilet to eat cat food put out for hedgehogs	Pontypool	35	15-Oct-06
Evening sighting - owner concerned about fish in pond. Local wildlife trust gave her reassurance.	Bomere Heath	40	29-Oct-06
Two or more juveniles photographed and videoed in garden, visiting to take cat food. Late litter?	Dayhouse Bank	37	05-Nov-06
Animal frequently entering house through cat flap at night. Got photos. Seems tame so likely to be ferret. Possibly more than one animal as different sizes.	Pontypool	41	25-Nov-06
Recovered from property and passed to International Ferret Welfare. Examined by JB in Jan 07 and judged to be wild polecat. Later released by RSPCA.	Bradmore	39	15-Dec-06

Appendix 5
The distribution by vice-county of new positive 10km squares (based on presence of verifiable polecat records) added during 2004-2006 to the polecat's 1959-1997 British distribution, shown in descending order for each country; vice-counties shaded in green contain >5 new 10km squares and represent the most active areas of recent range expansion by polecats.

Country and vice-county	No. new 10km squares 2004-2006
Scotland	**6**
Caithness	2
East Perth	2
East Sutherland	1
Lanark	1
Wales	**13**
Glamorgan	5
Monmouth	4
Anglesey	2
Denbigh	1
Flint	1
England	**111**
Derby	13
Dorset	9
North Wilts	8
Berks	8
Bucks	7
South Hants	7
North Hants	6
Bedford	5
Chester	5
Northants	4
South Wilts	4
Surrey	4
West Lancaster	4
West Sussex	4
North Somerset	3
Herts	2
Oxford	2
Stafford	2
Warwick	2
Cumberland	1
Cheviotland	1
East Gloucester	1
Leicester	1
Middlesex	1
Mid-West York	1
North Lincoln	1
North Essex	1
Nottingham	1
South Essex	1
West Gloucester	1
Westmorland	1